Contents

Crisis Resolution and Home Treatment

A practical guide

Edited by Patrick McGlynn

© The Sainsbury Centre for Mental Health 2006

ISBN: 1 870480 70 8

ISBN13: 978 1 870480 70 3

Published by
The Sainsbury Centre for Mental Health
134-138 Borough High Street
London SE1 1LB
Tel: 020 7827 8300
Fax: 020 7403 9482
www.scmh.org.uk

The Sainsbury Centre for Mental Health (SCMH) is a charity that works to improve the quality of life for people with severe mental health problems. SCMH was founded in 1985 by the Gatsby Charitable Foundation, one of the Sainsbury Family Charitable Trusts, from which it receives core funding. SCMH is affiliated to the Institute of Psychiatry at King's College, London.

A charitable company limited by guarantee registered in England and Wales no. 4373019
Charity registration no. 1091156

Design: www.intertype.com
Printing: Nuffield Press, UK

About the authors

Dr Christopher Bridgett is consultant psychiatrist with a crisis resolution team in South Kensington and Chelsea, where he has developed a special interest in the use of social systems interventions. With Dr John Hoult, he currently organises a regular discussion group in London for consultant psychiatrists working with crisis resolution and home treatment (CRHT) teams.

Martin Flowers is a psychiatric nurse who is currently community teams programme manager for the Care Services Improvement Partnership (CSIP) Eastern region. He has a long association with crisis resolution services and helped to create and manage services in Camden and Islington. He has worked with the CSIP London Development Centre and CSIP South East Region in the development and training of crisis resolution teams and has worked for some time with the Sainsbury Centre for Mental Health (SCMH).

Keith Ford is a registered mental health nurse and has worked in mental health services for over 20 years. In recent years he has specialised in crisis services and assertive outreach. He obtained a Masters degree at Teesside University in 2001. His MSc dissertation looked at practitioner skills within assertive outreach. Keith worked at SCMH from 2003 to 2006 delivering training across England and Wales. Before joining SCMH he was a specialist practitioner for assertive outreach at Tees and North East Yorkshire NHS Trust for four years.

Dr John Hoult is a consultant psychiatrist who pioneered the development of crisis resolution teams in Australia in the 1970s and 1980s. He was subsequently invited to the UK to set up teams in Birmingham and in Camden and Islington. John has worked extensively in the development and research of crisis resolution and assertive outreach services. He is currently developing crisis teams in North Essex and across East Anglia with CSIP Eastern Region.

Nina Lakhani has worked as a mental health nurse within acute services in Scotland, London and Australia since 1997 and with crisis resolution teams in London since 2002. She worked as a trainer with SCMH from 2004 to 2006, working with crisis resolution teams throughout the UK. She has also been involved in developing short training courses for crisis resolution and now delivers individually tailored programmes to developing and established teams. Her particular areas of interest are social systems interventions, facilitating early discharge, individual roles and responsibilities within teams, whole systems working and the role of practice development in training.

Patrick McGlynn worked as programme lead for crisis resolution for SCMH from 2001 to 2006, making a significant contribution to the national development and training of CRHT teams. During this time he was also seconded to CSIP Eastern Region where he worked as programme manager responsible for the development and ongoing support of a range of community teams in that region. He is a psychiatric nurse by background, and has worked extensively in CRHT services both as a practitioner and manager since 1990. From 1997 to 2001 he worked as acute services manager in Birmingham with responsibility for managing the home treatment team, the acute inpatient unit and the acute day hospital.

Kim Woodbridge has worked as a nurse, psychotherapist and senior lecturer. In recent years, she has specialised in values-based practice (VBP) in mental health care. Kim has developed and delivered training on VBP, studied practice and published a workbook, *Whose Values?* (Woodbridge & Fulford, 2004). She is currently completing a doctorate in 'Values-Based Practice (VBP) in Mental Health'. Her recent work has included examining the role of values-based practice in relation to the implementation of new mental health legislation and the national Delivering Race Equality programme. She has also played a key role in the development of leadership and empowerment training for people who have used mental health services.

Introduction

Patrick McGlynn

Background

Crisis resolution and home treatment (CRHT) teams provide intensive support at home for individuals experiencing an acute mental health crisis. They aim to reduce both the number and length of hospital admissions and to ease the pressure on inpatient units.

Crisis resolution is not a new concept, but we have only recently seen the development of a significant number of these teams in the UK with the implementation of the *National Service Framework for Mental Health* (NSF) (DH, 1999). The best-known exponent of crisis intervention is Gerald Caplan, who believed it to be a process where an individual in crisis moves between different stages of equilibrium and disequilibrium, and practitioners adapt their interventions to meet these changing needs (Caplan, 1964). Caplan's work has been developed further by Stein (Stein & Test, 1980) in Wisconsin, USA, and Hoult (1986) in Sydney, Australia, and more recently within the UK as outlined in the Mental Health Policy Guide (DH, 2001a) to focus specifically on individuals experiencing an acute mental health crisis.

It states that CRHT teams should target those individuals in severe mental health crisis who would otherwise be hospitalised. They should provide care for people in the least restrictive environment and with minimum disruption to their lives and:

❖ be available 24 hours a day, seven days a week;

❖ act as a 'gatekeeper' to acute mental health services, by rapidly assessing all those at risk of hospitalisation and making decisions about the care required;

❖ remain involved until the crisis has resolved and ensure that links with appropriate ongoing care services have been made.

Recent figures show that 343 CRHT teams now exist in the UK (Forrest, 2005), which would suggest that the target of 335 teams set in the NHS Plan (DH, 2000a) has been achieved.

Now that CRHT teams have been established, the challenge ahead is to make them work to their full potential and to sustain the initial enthusiasm and energy. They need workers with the skills, capabilities and knowledge to provide good-quality care for those in a mental health crisis, backed up by well-functioning systems and management. This guide has been produced to support CRHT teams to meet the challenges of the next phase of their existence and make a real difference to the lives of the people they were set up to help.

What does this book aim to do?

Over the past five years the Sainsbury Centre for Mental Health (SCMH) has played a significant role in supporting the development of CRHT teams nationally. This publication draws on our experiences of delivering training and practice development to CRHT teams and attempts to place the implementation of these teams within a wider framework of development and modernisation.

The implementation of CRHT teams has not taken place within a vacuum. Both national policy and emerging evidence of best practice have influenced the design of services and day-to-day clinical practice. The emerging themes of social inclusion (Social Exclusion Unit, 2004) and values-based practice (Woodbridge & Fulford, 2004) have without doubt challenged traditional models of practice, while the publication of *The Ten Essential Shared Capabilities* (NIMHE, 2004) that the workforce should acquire and *The 10 High Impact Changes* (CSIP, 2006) have major implications for the development of the whole mental health workforce.

CRHT teams are in an ideal position to deliver the objectives outlined in these publications and this theme is reflected upon throughout this guide. The chapters outline a wide range of challenges which require attention if CRHT teams are to move on from the implementation phase to developing a service that can be sustained and built upon in the future.

Crisis resolution and home treatment

In introducing this volume it seems important to make a brief comment on language and in particular the terms 'crisis resolution' and 'home treatment'. The policy implementation guidelines for CRHT teams (DH, 2001a) use these terms interchangeably, viewing them as functions within one team. Nationally, interpretation of this has proved to be diverse, with a number of services separating the functions and having a crisis resolution team and a home treatment team as separate entities. The logic behind this is unclear and for the purposes of this book, we would see the two functions being integral parts of the same team. In essence, crisis resolution is an outcome of providing home treatment.

Who is this book for?

This publication will be of interest to all those involved in the delivery of mental health services, in particular practitioners from CRHT teams, practitioners in the wider service, service managers responsible for the development of CRHT teams, educational bodies charged with meeting the training needs of the workforce and those involved in the planning and modernisation of future mental health services. We would urge that the practice issues outlined in this publication be considered within the context of local services so as to develop service improvement strategies which take account of both research evidence and experience.

Where to from here?

Research evidence suggests that when CRHT teams are shaped around specific service characteristics and principles they are more likely to reduce the number of admissions to hospital (by between 20% and 40%) and the length of stay for people who are admitted, and improve service users' experiences of acute mental health care (Minghella *et al.*, 1998).

The evidence base in support of this and other assumptions on which we have developed our services in the UK is growing. We now have a critical mass of CRHT teams from which to conduct evaluation to confirm or refute this belief, and by doing this we can help sustain and adapt the model as necessary.

I would like to thank all of those who have participated in this publication. It has been a lengthy task but the outcome has been worth the time invested. What has struck me in going through this process is how much time we spend reflecting on the past and how little on planning for the future. Now is the time to put this right. We have come a long way in the development of CRHT teams in the UK, but there is still much to learn and as time goes on we will need to adapt the policy guidelines for these and other teams to reflect the experience in delivery. What is essential is that every endeavour is made to ensure that the gains achieved by establishing CRHT teams are maximised and that the profile of the teams remains high.

About the chapters

Setting the scene

Dr John Hoult has considerable experience of establishing CRHT teams. In Chapter 1 he describes the evidence supporting the development of CRHT services and the key issues arising from our experience of developing these teams. He offers his thoughts on how we can sustain an approach that offers such obvious benefits to both service users and the whole mental health system.

The role of values in a crisis

Kim Woodbridge has done valuable work in promoting a better understanding of values and their impact on practice nationally. In Chapter 2 she describes an evaluation of a CRHT team and how the values espoused by members of the team translate into practice. Giving teams the time to explore their values and develop a values-based practice model to underpin their interventions will assist in developing a better understanding of the service user's perspective and ultimately improve practice.

Risk management

Assessing and managing risk is a day-to-day task of CRHT teams. In Chapter 3, Keith Ford and Patrick McGlynn have attempted to identify the context in which risk exists in CRHT. They argue that a realistic approach has to be taken that recognises the difficulties in measuring risk and that learns lessons from previous perceived 'failures' in risk management. They also argue that approaches to this must recognise the positive qualities and characteristics that individual service users and the teams possess, enabling a shift away from a risk-averse approach to developing positive risk-taking strategies.

The social systems approach

The social systems approach recognises the importance of social relationships in creating and maintaining good mental health. A breakdown in someone's social relationships may trigger or exacerbate a mental health crisis. Dr Christopher Bridgett has long championed the use of social systems intervention as a way of both understanding and working with acute mental health crisis. In Chapter 4 he argues that there is a need to identify and engage with an individual's social network in order to define the crisis and to assist in bringing it to a resolution. He identifies practical strategies for working with an individual's social network.

Facilitating early discharge from hospital

Facilitating early discharge from hospital has become a key function of CRHT teams and is currently attracting significant interest. Nina Lakhani has developed a systematic process for delivering this function and has put this process into action within a number of teams. In Chapter 5 she describes the rationale for developing this approach and identifies the practical application to the clinical setting.

The process of crisis resolution

Martin Flowers and Patrick McGlynn both have significant experience as practitioners, team managers and trainers of CRHT teams. In Chapter 6, they use a case study to work through a typical crisis resolution scenario from assessment to resolution, identifying the potential problems that may arise at each stage and the ways in which these may be managed. It highlights the need for CRHT teams to work as an integrated part of the 'whole system' of mental health care.

CHAPTER 1

Setting the scene

Dr John Hoult

In 2000 the Department of Health published the NHS Plan (DH, 2000a) in which it announced that there should be 335 crisis resolution teams covering the whole of England. After a slow start this target was achieved by 2005. The Department of Health also published guidelines (2001a) as to the size of these teams, with whom they should work and the principles and practices they should operate by. But it has become apparent that in many places these guidelines have not been adhered to. For example, by 2003/04 only 53% of the teams operating provided a 24-hour service (Glover *et al.*, 2006, in press). In addition, many teams either do not gatekeep admissions to acute inpatient care or have only a limited gatekeeping function (Garcia *et al.*, 2005).

Research evidence from both randomised controlled trials (RCTs) and non-randomised studies consistently points to the efficacy of crisis resolution and home treatment (CRHT) teams. Yet in many places the new teams are not as effective as was hoped. Why is this so? In most cases, the reason is either insufficient funding of the teams (i.e., too few staff to be able to make an impact) or a failure to follow the guidelines; frequently it is both.

Definition

A CRHT team is a team of mental health professionals which can respond to psychiatric emergencies and crises quickly and in the person's home. The team is able to support, treat and manage the person at home (and support their carers) until the crisis is resolved and the person is offered ongoing care.

Why do we do it?

CRHT teams have been developed for a number of reasons:

❖ It is humane to provide help as soon as possible to people who are in crisis.

❖ Interpersonal problems make a major contribution to many psychiatric crises. If people can stay at home at the time of crisis, team members can observe these problems first-hand, as most people behave more naturally in their own homes. The team can then work with the service user and their social network to address these problems. Hospital admission may initially take the heat out of interpersonal conflicts, but doctors do not have the opportunity to observe these conflicts and the care they offer centres on controlling behaviour and treating symptoms. The conflicts remain, to surface later and trigger another mental health crisis.

❖ Evidence repeatedly shows service users do not like hospitals (SCMH, 1998). They prefer to be treated at home or at least expect that a range of alternatives will have been considered prior to the decision to admit them to hospital (Gray & Baulcombe, 1996).

❖ Early intervention and treatment prevents deterioration and leads to quicker improvement.

❖ Being a psychiatric inpatient carries more social stigma than being treated at home.

❖ Home treatment has been shown to cost less than inpatient treatment. Up to 30% of inpatient costs are for hotel services such as cleaning, cooking, linen, etc., not to mention the capital cost of the building. This money is not available for clinical care (Young & Reynolds, 1981).

The evidence for CRHT

Research into the effectiveness of CRHT services has been limited and sporadic. This might be perceived to be a problem. Yet the evidence for the effectiveness of community mental health teams and for inpatient services is also very limited.

The best evidence for the effectiveness of any intervention in medicine (including psychiatry) is considered to come from RCTs. The Cochrane collaboration was established in 1993 (www.cochrane. org) to develop a database of systematic reviews on a wide range of interventions. As part of the Cochrane collaboration Joy et al. (2004) reviewed the five published RCTs on crisis intervention for people with severe mental illness, cautioning that none of the studies investigated crisis intervention in its pure form.

Two of the studies, Pasamanick et al. in Louisville, Kentucky (1967) and Fenton et al. in Montreal (1982), looked at teams that would not be considered to be practising CRHT as we understand it today. They excluded people who were considered to be dangerous or suicidal, used staff with no psychiatric training and did not have 24-hour availability. Nevertheless they did have outcomes favouring home intervention.

The other three studies were similar to each other, and are the basis for CRHT teams as recommended for England by the policy implementation guidelines (DH, 2001a). All included randomly allocated patients as they presented to a psychiatric hospital for admission; all included dangerous and suicidal individuals and excluded only those with brain damage, learning difficulties or a primary diagnosis of substance misuse; all provided mobile 24-hour support to the service users at home and to their families; and all had an adequately staffed, multidisciplinary team.

Stein and Test (1980) in Madison, Wisconsin, USA, had a team of 14 staff working with 65 patients whom they treated for 14 months. Only 12 patients were admitted to hospital in the first year, for an average of nine days, compared with 58 patients in the control group. People in the experimental group had fewer symptoms after 12 months, they spent more time employed and they were more satisfied. Costs were slightly higher for the experimental group.

The Sydney study (Hoult et al., 1983) had a team of seven staff plus a part-time psychiatrist for 60 service users who were treated for 12 months.

Four months after entering the study, experimental group service users had significantly lower symptom levels than the control group, and were significantly more pleased about the care they received. The relatives of people in the experimental group were more satisfied with treatment and 75% were pleased that the service user was not admitted (rising to 91% among carers who actually lived with the person). Overall, 40% of people in the experimental group had been admitted, compared with 97% of controls; an average of 8.4 bed days were used compared with 53.5 days, and there were no readmissions among this group, compared with half of those in the control group.

In London, Muijen et al. (1992) randomly allocated 189 service users. The experimental group spent an average of 18 days in hospital compared with the control group's 76 days, after 12 months.

Joy *et al.* (2004) concluded in their Cochrane review that: "[the evidence]... suggests that home care crisis treatment, coupled with an ongoing home care package, is a viable and acceptable way of treating people with serious mental illnesses". They stated that home care was slightly superior in avoiding repeat admissions, reduced loss to follow up, reduced family burden, and was a more satisfactory form of care for both patients and families.

Since the 2003 Cochrane update another RCT has been conducted by Johnson *et al.* (2005) in North Islington, an inner city district of London. In this RCT, 260 people who were experiencing a crisis severe enough for hospital admission to be considered were randomly allocated to a 24-hour CRHT team or to receive treatment as usual, without the option of CRHT.

The study showed that there was a highly significant reduction both in the number of people admitted to hospital in the CRHT group after eight weeks, and in the mean bed-days used. This reduction was still there after six months, implying that admission was prevented, and not just deferred.

The special research methodology requirements in RCTs mean that they happen in somewhat artificial conditions, not fully applicable to the real world. Other studies are able to produce results that enhance or modify our knowledge. The studies fall into two groups: studies of comparison areas and studies of before and after.

In two studies carried out in Sparkbrook, Birmingham, the CRHT function was not done by a separate team but by a community mental health team (CMHT). This study (Dean *et al.*, 1993) compared people living in two neighbouring areas, one of which provided home treatment and the other did not. The sample consisted of all of those having an acute episode severe enough to warrant hospital admission. Only 35% of those in Sparkbrook were admitted, for an average of 20.6 days over the 12-month study period, compared with 100% admitted for an average of 67.9 days for the neighbouring locality. There was no difference between the groups on clinical measures, but the service users and relatives in the Sparkbrook area preferred the CRHT approach and the relatives reported less of a burden.

One revealing study took place in Kalamazoo, Michigan, USA (Reding & Raphelson, 1995), demonstrating the value of having a senior psychiatrist with a commitment to CRHT work on the team. Prior to the psychiatrist's arrival the team functioned as a mobile crisis intervention service; after his arrival admissions to hospital dropped by 40%. When he departed they returned to their previous level.

The most recent before-and-after study was one in South Islington, London (Johnson *et al.*, 2005). Just before and just after the introduction of the CRHT team, people who met predetermined criteria for being in a mental health crisis were assessed at baseline and after six weeks. The admission rate in the six weeks after the CRHT intervention fell from 71% to 49%.

At the time of writing there has been no published, systematic, nationwide review of CRHT teams and therefore the national picture is unclear at present. In the East of England an informal audit of CRHTs has been carried out by the regional development centre. One important finding has been that, whereas previously most mental health services commonly paid for expensive emergency beds in private psychiatric clinics to take the overflow of acutely unwell people from the acute admission wards, in the space of two years (coinciding with the introduction of CRHT teams) this practice has stopped. Across the region, in areas served by 20 of the 28 new CRHT teams there has been either a reduction in admissions (up to 50% in some teams) or in bed use (up to 40%), or in both.

Can this kind of impact be sustained? Data as yet unpublished from a team in North Birmingham shows that the 50% reduction in admissions, which occurred soon after the team commenced, has been sustained over a ten-year period. Reduction in bed use has been harder to sustain. It is claimed that this is because of the significant number of supported accommodation facilities which have closed in this area in the latter part of the decade.

It is unclear as to whether this picture is reflected nationally, but anecdotally it appears that there are many areas where little has changed in terms of hospital admissions.

Key features of a successful CRHT team

Practical experience shows that certain features characterise well-functioning CRHT teams. These are discussed below:

Size and structure of a CRHT team

The ideal size for a CRHT team depends on:

❖ the population of the catchment area to be covered

❖ the level of need in the catchment area

❖ the number of inpatient admissions from the catchment area prior to the CRHT team commencing operation

❖ the number of staff needed to maintain an adequate rota, allowing for periods of leave and sickness

❖ the need for good communication between team members.

The policy implementation guidelines (DH, 2001a) state that there should be 14 clinical staff (not including medical staff) per 150,000 population but acknowledges that local circumstances mean a team may require a variation from this. Inner city areas may generate far more people in crisis for a given population size than do rural areas because the people living there tend to have more problems and fewer social supports. There is an argument therefore for inner city teams being larger or the population covered being smaller.

There are some areas – especially rural areas with small populations – where to follow the guidelines would result in a team with too few staff for an adequate rota. With fewer than 10 or 11 staff a team becomes vulnerable to the effects of holidays and study leave plus unexpected sickness, with the possibility of having only one worker for a particular shift – a situation which could be dangerous. From the experience of the early teams, a team of 14 can deal with an area that produces about 400 hospital admissions per annum before the team's commencement.

In some areas of the country there are teams that are quite large, with more than 30 staff covering a population of around 350,000. This can create potential problems with staff communication; team handovers need to be handled with firmness and skill, for example, to ensure that they do not take an inordinate amount of time. Nevertheless some of the larger teams have produced good outcomes, so it is too early to say whether they should be recommended or not.

Gatekeeping to hospital beds

We can see no evidence of CRHT teams, nationally or internationally, being effective in achieving reductions in hospital bed use if they do not have the right to gatekeep, i.e. to assess most or all referrals prior to hospital admission. This issue has probably resulted in more friction than anything else between teams and between professional groups, but is one of the most critical for CRHT teams. It therefore has to be addressed, however uncomfortable the process may appear.

It is logical to assume that if a CRHT team is expected to reduce the pressure on acute inpatient units by 30%, as suggested in the NHS Plan (DH, 2000a), the team must focus on those who would have been admitted to hospital if it had not existed. To do so the team has to target anyone at risk of hospitalisation. Without the gatekeeping role, other professionals may continue admitting as before, and few cases may be referred to the CRHT team.

All users of mental health services who are at risk of hospitalisation should have the right to assessment for treatment at home and for this reason gatekeeping should be absolute and extend to all assessments for hospital admission, including Mental Health Act assessments and assertive outreach cases. It is recognised, however, that on occasion the team may be unable to carry out an assessment because of the timescales involved, and in such cases the involvement of the CRHT team should not hold up the process.

Twenty-four-hour availability

There is much debate as to the need for teams to be available 24 hours a day. Some say it costs too much to run, others that there is no call for it in their area, but there is a clear rationale for ensuring that this is a core characteristic of CRHT teams. There are two main reasons for providing this.

The first is that new referrals can turn up at any hour, not just obligingly during the daytime. At night most referrals will come from A&E and the number will vary according to how busy the department is, but the people who attend will be in some degree of crisis. Failure to gatekeep admissions at night may lead to a disproportionate number of admissions taking place during this period.

The second reason is that many of the service users who are supported by the team would otherwise be in hospital. In view of the acute nature of their difficulties, the service users and their carers need someone they can turn to should a difficulty arise, especially in the middle of the night when people feel most alone. If they know they can get immediate help at any time of the day or night they will be more willing to accept home treatment. So while most teams are infrequently or even rarely called out at night, the person on call may get more phone calls from both service users and carers. The team member, having both knowledge of the service user and a home treatment ethos, will often be able to resolve the matter on the phone. The knowledge that staff can be contacted at any time, and if necessary come out, is of great reassurance to service users and carers. It is important to note that a team that does not provide a 24-hour service cannot claim to gatekeep hospital admissions comprehensively.

Clearly defined target population

The main focus for CRHT teams is on people with schizophrenia, those with bipolar affective disorders and severe depression, and people with borderline personality disorders. One area of controversy is the relationship that CRHT teams have with A&E departments. An unpublished survey at the Norfolk and Norwich hospital in 2005 revealed that about 90% of patients whom mental health services were asked to see in the A&E department did not require the CRHT team service. Ideally A&E departments should have their own mental health liaison service to deal with requests for mental health assessments and only pass on to the CRHT team cases at risk of admission to the psychiatric unit. CRHT teams can have a helpful role in supporting non-target groups in crisis for a few days until they can be passed on to other community-based services. Unfortunately, in too many areas, CRHT teams are used to undertake all A&E mental health work, to the detriment of their capacity to deliver home treatment.

Rapid, mobile response

The sooner a problem can be dealt with and treatment commences, the shorter the period of suffering and the less likely deterioration is to occur. It is thus essential that the team is mobile. There are some people who will not come to a clinic or a centre or an A&E department, despite everyone's efforts to get them there, because they do not believe they need help, or they do not want help. Seeing people in their own environment allows them to be more natural, more of their social network is likely to be involved and staff can evaluate the circumstances in which treatment is to take place. A problem with A&E assessments is that service users and carers sometimes have an expectation that admission to hospital will be the next step, and even if staff do not think this is warranted, time and effort has to be expended to overcome that view.

Medical input

There is no doubt that doctors have a vital role to play in these services, having traditionally had a central role in gatekeeping hospital beds. It would seem important to optimise the use of this experience in the decision-making processes around admission to hospital. Department of Health guidance into new ways of working for psychiatrists has recognised the challenges to the traditional psychiatrist role brought about by the modernisation of services (including the creation of CRHT teams). The guidance suggests that psychiatrists should be at the forefront of this culture change and it clearly indicates a desire to have a clearer, more focused role for psychiatrists within the context of functional multidisciplinary teams:

> " *New ways of working are about using the skills, knowledge and experience of consultant psychiatrists to best effect by concentrating on service users with the most complex needs, acting as a consultant to multidisciplinary teams and promoting distributed responsibility and leadership across teams to achieve a cultural shift in services.* " *(DH, 2005)*

The role of the psychiatrist in relation to a CRHT team is detailed in Box 1.

Box 1: The role of the psychiatrist in relation to a CRHT team

❖ **Diagnosis:** Effective management and treatment depends on accurate assessment of biological, psychological and social factors.

❖ **Prescribing:** Available to quickly prescribe medication for a person in an emotionally distressed state.

❖ **Clinical leadership:** The psychiatrist is often the most highly trained professional on the team and has (or should have) the most clinical knowledge. This does not invalidate other members' contributions but complements them.

❖ **Dealing with complex cases**

❖ **The doctor–patient relationship:** There will be occasions when service users and carers want to meet with the doctor, to discuss diagnosis and the treatment plan specifically with them.

❖ **Medico-legal problems:** The consultant psychiatrist should be involved in discussions of this nature.

❖ **Representing the team to other doctors:** Any new service will encounter resentment and hostility from some doctors. The most effective person to deal with the attitudes of other doctors can be the doctor associated with the CRHT team.

❖ **Representing the team to management**

❖ **Involvement in the training of other staff**

Expectation of managing people's care at home

If there is not this expectation when the team goes to visit a client, then the likelihood is that the team will become little more than a funnel to hospital. This expectation means that the team will keep talking to the person in crisis, searching for some aspect with which to engage, both on an emotional level and in rational dialogue. This can take an hour or two and may not always happen; but the expectation should always be there.

Involvement of social network at every phase

There are mutually beneficial reasons for involving the social network. The network can give important information about the client that the client does not disclose. It will help the team to assess the impact of the various members on the client (and the client's impact on them) and find out problems that need to be addressed. The network can help in planning what interventions to make and in implementing those interventions through monitoring and providing practical and emotional support. CRHT teams in turn should inform, advise, educate and generally support the social network.

A client's crisis is rarely due to the illness alone; almost always there is an interplay between the individual and their social network.

Spending prolonged time with the client initially

Initial assessments can be lengthy affairs. Not only has a history to be taken from the service user and the social network, but a disturbed person may have to be engaged and calmed down. Then planning options have to be considered and a plan agreed. All this takes time if it is to be done properly. Hours will probably elapse, even for a service user who is familiar with the team. Because their focus is on crisis work, CRHT teams are able to do this. It is time well spent because it allows a therapeutic relationship between the team and the service user and their social network to develop. Teams should not be frightened of spending a lot of time on the initial assessment.

Visiting frequently in the early stages

Many of the people taken on by the CRHT team would otherwise be in hospital, where their behaviour and mental state would be frequently monitored. These also need to be monitored when they are receiving home treatment. Practical and interpersonal problems may need to be addressed. It may be necessary to obtain further history.

Most importantly, the therapeutic relationship needs to be built upon with the service user and their carers to enable them to develop trust and confidence in the CRHT team. If this is their first experience of the CRHT team they will understandably be wary of what is happening; they will not have had such an intensity of home visiting offered (or given) to them in the past so they may be unsure whether it will be delivered. Frequent visiting helps to overcome this apprehension and any concern that team members have about the person's welfare.

A person who is very unwell will be visited twice or even three times daily in the beginning. As their condition improves, so the frequency of visiting can be reduced.

Addressing practical problems

To survive in the community a person needs money, food, shelter and utility supplies. CRHT teams must address these issues at the beginning of their involvement with the person in crisis. Sometimes they have to buy food, charge an electricity key, lend a person some money or arrange accommodation on the first day. On subsequent days they may have to organise benefits, arrange emergency house repairs, help clean up, take the person for blood tests or to a GP appointment – whatever needs to be done to help that person survive in the community.

Medication management

In the initial phase, medication can calm disturbed behaviour quickly and, importantly, allow everyone to get a good night's sleep. As in a hospital, its effects need to be monitored in case the initial dose is too high or too low and, as in hospital, it is sometimes necessary to make sure that it is really being taken. Where medication is seen as a key element of an individual's care package, the team may have to monitor compliance closely and, indeed, where situations are chaotic the team may need to take control of dispensing.

Disturbed behaviour may have to be controlled quickly if a person is to remain in the community before the social network becomes worn out and neighbours become frustrated. Ensuring that everyone has a good night's sleep is often a big help in de-escalating a crisis situation.

Criticism has been made that some CRHT teams offer little more than medication monitoring. This may be due to inadequate staffing of teams. In 1997 the Mental Health Act Commission reported that the amount of direct patient contact by staff on wards is often low (SCMH/MHAC, 1997). CRHT staff must engage properly with people on their caseload.

Giving advice, guidance, information, education and counselling

A CRHT team should spend time talking to service users and their social networks; it is one of the most therapeutic things they can do. One of the most frequent complaints made about mental health services in general is how little time health professionals spend with service users and how little information they provide. The daily visits should not be just cursory affairs; staff should be making regular enquiries about the person's symptoms, functioning, social interactions, relationships and whatever is relevant. Carers should be asked for their comments on the above, and about how it is affecting them. Both service users and carers need information about the illness and its course, prognosis and treatment.

Staying involved until the crisis is resolved and ensuring handover to ongoing care

CRHT teams keep working with a person until their crisis has been resolved. The team then makes sure the person is handed over formally to ongoing care, usually to the CMHT. The reasons for doing this are to prevent rapid relapse and to try to make sure the person's needs and problems are addressed as far as possible.

Sustainability

No service has a divine right to exist and if it isn't able to convince others of its usefulness then it will be unlikely to survive: either being swiftly disbanded or allowed to slowly haemorrhage. CRHT teams are no exception. Factors that can help them to achieve sustainability include:

Make an impact

The quickest way to demonstrate an impact in order to sustain a CRHT service is to reduce admissions and bed use. It is quick and easy to collect this data, and there is little cost involved. CRHT teams should keep data on their performance to monitor progress, identify blockages and plan for the future.

Provide adequate staffing

No team can sustain an adequate service for long without adequate staffing. New referrals can occur at any time and may take up three or four hours of a worker's time. Meanwhile there is a caseload to be visited, monitored and be given time, and family members to be interviewed. In order to build and maintain a therapeutic relationship, it is essential that staff spend time with the service user and their social network. The team must have enough staff available to do this.

Offer a good service

Some CRHT teams are seen as unfriendly and overly bureaucratic. Their referral criteria are not clear and they are perceived as unhelpful, treating referrers as the enemy. They do not apologise, they are hard to contact, they don't communicate, they don't explain things to service users and their social networks, and they want to send service users too quickly back to the care of the CMHT. A team that is polite, helpful and responsive will get support from service users, carers and other health professionals.

CRHT team managers must make sure these elementary matters are observed by all staff.

Remember the CRHT team is just one part of a wider service

While it is natural and good for team morale that the team should applaud its own work, CRHT teams can only be effective as part of a wider system of services in which all of the components need each other and need to work together.

Often the arrival of a new CRHT team will bring to light practices in other teams that are undesirable; for example, that clients with severe mental health problems are seen very infrequently by their care co-ordinator. Such discoveries need to be handled tactfully and with understanding. Mental health professionals in all parts of the service want to help people and will change their practice if the transition is managed appropriately.

Ensure good leadership

Just as for any team, the CRHT team leader has to inspire the staff, maintain their morale, ensure that the team knows the vision and that bad practice is identified early and dealt with. A problem in CRHT teams can be the gradual drift away from doing time-consuming and uncomfortable tasks, such as involving and dealing with the social network, and from being willing to manage risk. The danger is that the team will come to deal primarily with medication monitoring. The leader has to be alert to this drift and take steps to remedy it. A good leader needs to share some clinical work with the team to understand their work and to help with difficult cases. The leader also has to deal effectively on the team's behalf with the rest of the mental health system and with senior managers within the trust.

Arrange for continued staff training

Most teams are able to have a few weeks' initial training before they start work. This helps them to bond as a team and teaches them new ways of understanding and working with acute crises. The new team, it is hoped, will apply these new attitudes and skills when they commence, but after a while staff leave and new staff join who have not had this training. Teams have to find time to train new staff and refresh the skills of existing staff.

Meet with other CRHT teams

Staff from the team should attend CRHT team forums to exchange information about the good things teams have done, and the hazards teams have faced, to support each other and to unite to take action to deal with threats to their sustainability.

Conclusion

There is now a justified expectation that CRHT teams nationwide will deliver what the research and the early teams demonstrated could be delivered, namely a decrease in admissions and an increase in service-user satisfaction. A fully resourced, well-functioning team that adheres to the model used by successful teams in the past should have little trouble in achieving this. An under-funded, poorly organised team that strays too far from the model will struggle to make an impact. Too many teams not making any impact will imperil the sustainability of a type of service which evidence shows can make an impact for the better. The challenge of setting up crisis teams across the country has been met successfully. But new challenges exist which will require constant attention if we are to sustain what has been achieved and consider further development.

CHAPTER 2

The role of values in a crisis

Kim Woodbridge

Introduction

❝ *The team is closely following the Policy Implementation Guidelines but it is not working, there's just something missing...* ❞

(Senior manager)

❝ *It's about the process. The outcomes we are aiming for can be the same; it's how we get there that's different.* ❞

(Home treatment team leader)

What is it that is missing from some crisis resolution and home treatment (CRHT) teams but not others? What is it about the process that is different? It is quite likely that the answer has something to do with values.

People's values differ enormously: what may be important to one individual may be of little significance to another. It may be difficult to define values or to prove their existence, but they are present in all situations. Values can be seen as underpinning and overlapping with many other areas. They are present in mental health practice, within individuals and within the dynamics of a relationship.

CRHT teams face conflicting pressures every day in meeting the demands of diverse values in their practice. It is important that they understand how these values relate to, interact with and affect experiences, actions and relationships in mental health care.

Values-based practice

Values-based practice enables practitioners to work in a respectful and sensitive way with the different values and perspectives that they encounter in their work. In today's complex world, they must be able to work effectively with unfamiliar situations in unfamiliar contexts. They need not only competence but capability in their work (see Box 1).

Box 1: Capable practice

Competence – what individuals know or are able to do in terms of knowledge, skills and attitudes.

Capability – the extent to which individuals can adapt to change, generate new knowledge and continue to improve their practice.

(Adapted from Fraser & Greenhalgh, 2001)

Values-based practice supports capable practice by providing a process that can be used in situations where there are complex problems with no ready answers. Therefore, in conjunction with evidence-based practice, it underpins the ten essential shared capabilities (ESCs) that all mental health workers need in their practice (see Box 2).

Box 2: The ten essential shared capabilities (ESCs) for mental health practice

1. Working in partnership

2. Respecting diversity

3. Practising ethically

4. Challenging inequality

5. Promoting recovery

6. Identifying people's needs and strengths

7. Providing service user-centred care

8. Making a difference

9. Promoting safety and positive risk taking

10. Personal development and learning.

NIMHE, 2004

There are many ways to work with values, and plenty of books and workshops on the subject. There are two main advantages to using the values-based practice referred to here. First, it provides a framework and the skills to enable people to work in a respectful and sensitive way with the perspectives present in everyday practice. Second, it's a way of working with values rather than imposing any predetermined values. Therefore it provides a way of actively closing the gap between stated values and what actually happens. It is not about creating a new set of directives or ethics codes for staff.

Values-based practice can be defined in different ways. The one we have used is:

❝ *Values-based practice (VBP) is the theory and skills base for effective health care decision making where different (and hence potentially conflicting) values are in play.* ❞

Fulford, 2004.

To understand what this means for everyday practice it is useful to look at the ten pointers to good process that underpin values-based practice (see Box 3).

Box 3: The ten key pointers to good process in values-based practice

1. **Awareness:** To raise awareness of the values present in each situation.

2. **Reasoning:** There are many powerful ways of reasoning about values, including revealing the values present in our own reasoning.

3. **Knowledge:** It is important to get as much information about what is known about values in any situation. This includes using evidence-based research knowledge.

4. **Communication:** Because there has to be a sharing of the values in the decision making process, communication is central to all of the principles of values-based practice.

5. **Service user centred:** The first source for information on values in each situation is the perspective of the service user concerned.

6. **Multiperspective:** Conflicts of values are resolved not by applying a 'pre-prescribed rule' but by working towards a balance of different perspectives.

7. **Facts and values:** All decisions are based on facts and values.

8. **Values are only noticed, however, when there is conflict** – 'dis-census' rather than consensus.

9. **Increasing scientific knowledge is leading to an increasing role for values in decision making.**

10. **Partnership:** Decisions are made through people working together and in partnership.

Overall the aim of values-based practice is to start with respect for differences between people. It relies on the existence of 'good process' to achieve a balance of values in decision making.

This chapter is an introduction to values-based practice in the context of CRHT team work. A full description of values-based practice can be found in *Whose Values? A workbook for values-based practice in mental health care* (Woodbridge & Fulford, 2004).

What are values?

Although we can all agree that values exist and we understand what we mean when we say 'values', actually defining them is not easy. However, it is useful to consider some of the existing attempts to define them. Values are:

❖ "Standards of behaviour" (Oxford University Press, 2001)

❖ "Persons are ... continually regarding things as good or bad, pleasant or unpleasant, beautiful or ugly, appropriate or inappropriate, true or false, virtues or vices. Values serve as criteria for action; they become criteria for judgement, preference and choice." (Rokeach,1973)

❖ "Values is a term used in different ways. One is relating to a thing's fitness for purpose, for example a 'good' pen or a 'good' computer." (Sharpe,1997)

❖ "By patient values we mean the unique preferences, concerns and expectations each patient brings to a clinical encounter and which must be integrated into clinical decisions if they are to serve the patient." (Sackett *et al.*, 2000).

Values come in many varieties such as moral values (as in what is good), personal preferences and aesthetic values (as in what is beautiful). Also values often exist either as contradictions or in conflict. For example, the values originally underpinning the NHS have been identified as:

❖ Health
❖ Universalism
❖ Equity
❖ Democracy
❖ Respect for human dignity
❖ Public service
❖ Efficiency

(New, 1999)

However, since the 1980s, as a result of political initiatives, these founding values have been combined with:

❖ Choice
❖ Competition
❖ Private sector provision
❖ Management techniques
❖ Cost effectiveness
❖ Value for money (a driver for evidence-based practice).

(New, 1999)

Although in theory it may be possible to work with both sets of values, in practice it is likely that the second set will conflict with the aspirations of the first.

Raising awareness, looking for values

The first step towards good process in values-based practice is to raise awareness of the values present in any situation. A good way of doing this is to look at language. Language is very important in mental health. The language people use can lead to greater understanding or can be a barrier. Service users and carers frequently refer to the excluding nature of the use of technical terms, jargon and abbreviations in discussion with mental health staff.

Being aware of the values we communicate either verbally or in writing is a difficult task, as they are as natural as breathing. Even with the best intentions we are often surprised by what we may have communicated when we really examine the language we used.

Box 4 shows an extract from a crisis resolution guide produced by SCMH in 2001. It is helpful to look for the values within it and consider their implications.

Box 4: Identifying values in a crisis resolution document

This is an extract from a document describing key principles in crisis resolution.

1. Crisis management is a process of working through the crisis to the point of resolution.

2. Successful client engagement is paramount. The formation of a therapeutic alliance with the client is essential before any interventions can be successful.

3. Services take a holistic approach, looking at all the factors involved in the crisis, including biological, psychological and social issues, and using a range of interventions to address these.

4. The individual's social network has a powerful effect on the person's mental health and treatment must directly address these significant social issues.

5. Crisis staff should approach work with users from a 'strengths' rather than an 'illness' model, and draw on the innate strengths of service users in order to support them.

6. Educating the service user will comprise a significant part of the crisis work and should help clients learn behaviours to improve and maintain their mental health. The approach should be one of collaborating with the user or their family by 'doing work with them', rather than 'doing work on them', so as to promote their 'ownership' of the crisis.

(SCMH, 2001)

Different readers have found different values in this document. Key words and phrases that reveal what is to be valued include:

1. 'a process' and 'to the point of resolution'

2. 'engagement' and 'before interventions'

3. 'holistic' and 'range of interventions'

4. 'individual's social network' and 'must address social issues'

5. 'work from service users' strengths', 'innate strengths' and 'not illness model'

6. 'education', 'learning', 'behavioural change', 'working with' and 'service user owning the crisis'.

There is a frequent use of the term 'interventions' which holds associated professional values and meaning. There is also a possible contradiction of values between the fifth principle, which emphasises the importance of not working from an 'illness model', and the fourth, which talks about 'treatment' and thus suggests the opposite.

It is interesting that there is an emphasis in the crisis resolution guide on the service being about the 'relationship' and 'working with' the service user, but the language used includes many professional terms; for example, 'social network' and 'behavioural change'. Often, a value such as 'working with' may be expressed in a document, but the language of the document does not reflect this.

This is just an example of how values can be explored in language. Once these are part of a team's awareness it is easier to discuss them with colleagues, carers and service users. To gain more understanding of how people work with values in practice, a small pilot study was carried out with the East Towers Home Treatment Team in East London.

The East Towers CRHT values study

The aim of the study was not to judge the team's values against the values they were supposed to have but to find out what they valued and how they worked with diverse and conflicting values. What follows is a snapshot of what was valued by seven of the team members of the East Towers Home Treatment Team. The interviewees were from a variety of backgrounds, culturally and professionally. They included both men and women, in their 30s and 40s. They held a range of positions in the team. The team became operational in June 2003 and the interviews took place later that year.

The team approach

All members interviewed made very positive statements about their experience of working with service users and colleagues as part of the CRHT team.

> *It's really interesting … I'm doing much more of an emotionally demanding job than I was doing in my last job … but it's less stressful because the team is good at sharing responsibility. I know when I'm not there the client's care will be just the same …*

Team member

The team approach provided support and a sharing of responsibility in making difficult decisions and working with complex cases. The team worked in a highly challenging and emotionally charged environment but this approach reduced stress and feelings of burn-out. It also provided a range of different ideas and perspectives useful for problem solving and making decisions.

At the same time as valuing the team, individuals equally valued their differences (personal and professional) and individual autonomy.

The team members were thus able to cope with the challenge of having different opinions and ways of viewing work with clients. Valuing their differences enabled tolerance, understanding and sustained positive relationships within the team after disagreements about a person's care. The team approach developed because staff were there for each other when working under difficult conditions such as the middle of the night or high-risk situations. The opportunity to meet in social situations outside work also reduced tension between those who had strong differences of opinion at work.

Self-awareness

> *When I sat down and talked about it, in supervision, I was really stuck in my values. I thought, we're all the same, as much as we say, oh, I'm willing to take on board other people's values, really in the back of our minds we think – but my values are right, my values are objective and right.*

Team members needed self-awareness in order to cope with the differing views of what the problems were and what should be done in a situation. It enabled the individual to step back and to recognise their own values and how they were imposing them on the others. It also enabled them to be more sensitive to others' views and to tolerate and to consider more objectively the other person's perspective, i.e., that of colleagues, service users and the relatives and friends of service users.

An equal voice in team meetings

> *I think it's unique that in the crisis teams, more than any other teams I've seen, everyone has got a fairly equal voice.*

Team members all referred to the importance of feeling that their opinions were equally respected regardless of their backgrounds.

" *One of the nicest things about being a worker on a crisis team is the fact that when you do actually see the client, on the whole you do spend really good quality time with them and you do sit down and work the issues through.* "

Values

" *I think values are extremely relevant. I don't think we have given enough attention to them.* "

All those interviewed felt that values had a key impact on the team. The main comment was that values were not properly addressed, and that there should be more work in this area. Suggestions included:

❖ Trying to answer the questions, "Do values help us in our work and our relationships with clients?", "How often do we really address issues such as faith, spirituality, gender and culture?", "Why doesn't values-based practice happen?"

❖ More training in values-based practice and working with diverse values. Some interviewees had previously completed values activities which had raised awareness of how diverse the team's values were and had been very useful in stimulating thought and reflection.

❖ Discussing values in group supervision, although there were some concerns about how this could be made a productive and safe process.

❖ Looking at the role of professional values within the team.

❖ Developing a team philosophy to clarify the team's core values.

Other things that staff valued about the team included:

❖ The process itself. For example, the outcome may be about taking medication but what was important was how the team worked with the client. The process should be flexible, and tailored to the service user, using negotiation rather than coercion.

" *I always say yes, you have difficulties, but you are the best person to solve your problem, you've got the inner resources, you know. Make the person feel valued and respected, and have some sort of control or sort of responsibility. Then see that person as a human being who could be me or you.* "

❖ Recognising the importance of perceiving progress in an individual using the service. This may be in very small steps. Any change in the service user's attitude or behaviour was considered by the team to be beneficial to that individual.

" *It's very dynamic as well, that's one thing I like, it's very dynamic, and you're able to see people getting well.* "

The issue of resistance and engagement was a strong theme and could have a significant impact on the team's morale and perceptions of its success or failure. How values and working with values play a part in these areas needs further consideration and exploration.

Dealing with conflicts

When there are conflicts, team members said they would:

❖ get more information

❖ jointly visit with the two people who are seeing the situation differently

❖ find a compromise, a 'middle of the road' solution

❖ try to find some level of informal agreement, even though the disagreements could not be formally resolved, in order for the work to move on.

Other comments related to conflicts within the team. Disagreements were often over when to stop working with a service user, or over what was the business of the CRHT team and what was not. Learning from previous arguments was said to be important, to avoid repeating them again and again.

❝ *I think if you're going to have a healthy sort of work environment, you do have to take that on board and realise that you're not perfect, you do make mistakes.* ❞

What was not mentioned was the importance of service user involvement that goes beyond expressing their preferences when using the service. But there were no routine mechanisms for service users to directly influence the development or delivery of the service through either evaluation or consultation.

Service user values in relation to CRHT

The Bristol User Focused Monitoring (UFM) group interviewed 65 people who had experienced a mental health crisis in the previous two years. They had a range of diagnoses including depression, anxiety, schizophrenia, psychosis and bipolar affective disorder. Most had used the services of a crisis team or community mental health team (CMHT). The study focused on their 'experience' of crisis and the help they had sought as well as the help they had actually received (Bristol Mind, 2004).

User-focused monitoring is a type of research undertaken by local service users and survivors. It aims to improve the quality and diversity of mental health services in an area. In Bristol, community care and crisis services were identified by service users as the most important areas to study.

The report looked at what crisis means to people, what causes crisis, the experience of crisis, the use of care/crisis plans, sources of help and people's own methods of coping.

It found that people wanted greater emotional support in a crisis. Emotional support was particularly valued as crisis was generally explained by service users as 'a feeling'. What they received was mostly medication. They wanted their experience to be given more respect and empathy, especially by medical staff. This perceived lack of understanding was seen as a lack of acknowledgement of their crisis.

Non-mental health workers, such as police and A&E staff, needed more training and operational procedures that reflected a better understanding of mental health needs and the rights of service users.

The report called for more information to be made available to service users. It found that service users' involvement in their own care planning was limited: fewer than half had a plan and, of those, only a few said the plan was followed during their crisis. Overall, service users lacked the knowledge and understanding about the care/crisis planning process and the option to make informed choices was limited by the lack of quality information made available to them.

It was important to involve families and friends as they had a key role to play. It was important that families and friends also received help and support during a crisis.

Links were drawn between the lack of informed service user involvement in their care planning, the lack of understanding and empathy of those with whom the service user had initial contact during a crisis and the proportion of service users who felt that their crisis could have been prevented.

According to the report, a high proportion of service users saw crisis teams as being helpful, meeting their needs, respecting their rights and wishes, and showing empathy. It was suggested in the report that this was the reason that over two-thirds of respondents said they felt they could 'tell the whole story' to members of the crisis team.

Conclusion

At the time of the East Towers study, there were several shared values between the crisis team members and the service users interviewed in the Bristol UFM report.

The best way to start working with values is to ask questions. These might include:

❖ What are our values?

❖ What is the purpose of our team?

❖ If we look at what we do first in a situation and what we talk about, what is it that we value most? What is top of the value hierarchy?

When a team starts out it may have a vision of an inclusive and holistic approach to care. Over time, through various demands and pressures, the focus can narrow to a service built around the taking of medication. By continually asking questions and revisiting the issues of values, it is possible to be aware of these changes and therefore to have more insight and control over them.

Building values into a CRHT team is a never-ending process, which requires continuous examination of the team's vision, values and actions, and how these three are in tune or at odds with each other.

This final quote from a team member gives an indication of the everyday complexity of values in mental health practice and yet how little time is spent on addressing them:

66 *Let me think – there's culture, faith, social care, health care, different policies, empowerment, service user involvement, working with families, carers, voluntary organisations, charities, age, being a man or a woman, recovery, social inclusion, all the other parts of the service, different parts of the community, a person's history, their hopes, all different values all affecting us, affecting what we do, what we think. I think we should really talk about values more ...* 99

CHAPTER 3

Risk management

Keith Ford and Patrick McGlynn

Introduction

Hospital admission is often sought for someone who is experiencing an acute mental health crisis after assessment of the potential risks of supporting them at home. The 1983 Mental Health Act states that compulsory admission may be sought where an individual is at risk of harm to self or others. This chapter looks at how risk is assessed and managed in crisis resolution and home treatment (CRHT) teams.

The measurement of risk in mental health services

Morgan (2000) defined measurement of risk as being "the likelihood of an event happening with potentially harmful or beneficial outcomes for self and/or others". This definition would surprise many working in mental health services in that it suggests there are potential beneficial outcomes to risk management, a concept which on the whole does not match with practitioners' perceptions as to the implications of risk behaviour.

Outside mental health care, risk is seen to have potential positive outcomes and therefore to enhance an organisation or an individual's position. This view is supported by Morgan who suggests that, without risk, there is no change, no development and no learning. It follows therefore that some form of risk in managing a case is essential for a positive outcome and that "a strategy of total risk avoidance could lead to excessively restrictive management, which may in itself be damaging to the individual" (Ministry of Health for New Zealand, 1998).

Risk is overwhelmingly viewed by mental health practitioners as a negative concept invoking concerns about accountability and blame for high-profile tragedies such as homicides and suicides. Reviewing the literature, there is a suggestion that risk management has focused very much on these low frequency and high consequence incidents. Yet the reality of risk is that the majority of it is high frequency and low consequence. We would not suggest that lessons cannot be learned from high consequence incidents, just that focusing all effort on reducing high consequence incidents undervalues the risk and the implications of risk for those living with it all the time.

Petch (2001) expresses concerns as to the over-emphasis on risk management within mental health services arguing that: "Such targeting results in altered perception of the public, politicians and the press that people suffering from mental illness are dangerous, despite the rate of such violence being essentially unchanged."

This view is supported by Szmukler (2003), who warns that risk assessment may emphasise control and containment at the expense of treatment and consequently "deter people who would benefit from mental health services, including 'risky' persons, from seeking help for fear of coercive treatments". There are also serious questions about the ability of practitioners to predict high-risk behaviour.

Having reviewed the literature Petch (2001) suggests that generally risk assessment tools "will be of limited usefulness and will always be of limited value in predicting rare events accurately".

Despite this, few would disagree with the need for risk assessment and management within a modern mental health service. But we need to look at the expected outcomes of such processes. Morgan (2000) suggests that accurate prediction and risk elimination are unreasonable benchmarks for measuring effectiveness, and that improved prediction rates and harm minimisation would be more realistic measures. Kennedy (2001) suggests that:

> " *Risk assessment is worth the effort and can be improved on, although only by recognising that the process of assessment is, for practical purposes, inseparable from the process of managing risk by matching the patient's risk to the appropriate level of therapeutic security.* "

Box 1: Findings about risk management in mental health services

Modernising Mental Health Services: Safe, Sound and Supportive

- ❖ Inadequate care, poor management of resources and under funding
- ❖ The proper range of services not always being available to provide the care and support people need
- ❖ Service users not remaining in contact with services
- ❖ Families who have willingly played a part in providing care have been overburdened
- ❖ Problems in recruiting and retaining staff
- ❖ The legal framework has failed to support effective treatment outside hospital.

(DH, 1998)

Other themes from inquiries into high risk incidents in mental health services

- ❖ Failures in communication, between and within agencies
- ❖ Failure to achieve multidisciplinary working
- ❖ Misinterpretation of the boundaries of professional confidentiality
- ❖ Poor co-ordination of complex care packages.

(Morgan & Hemming, 1999)

Some recommendations of Safety First: Five Year Report of the National Confidential Inquiry into Suicide and Homicide by People with Mental Illness

- ❖ Staff training in the management of risk – both suicide and homicide – every 3 years.
- ❖ All patients with severe mental illness and a history of self harm or violence to receive the most intensive level of care.
- ❖ Individual care plans to specify the action to be taken if patient is non compliant or fails to attend.
- ❖ Prompt access to services for patients in crisis and for their families.
- ❖ Assertive outreach teams to prevent loss of contact with vulnerable and high risk patients.

(DH, 2001d)

The failures of risk management

At this juncture it is important to reflect on why 'risk' has become such a key part of mental health policy and to consider examples of how government policy has been developed and its implications for services. During the late 1990s in particular there was an increased focus on mental health services. As secretary of state for health, Frank Dobson famously claimed that community care had failed in a number of ways and a number of reports were published which focused on the shortcomings of mental health services. Box 1 on page 34 summarises the key issues that emerged at that time.

One of the main drivers for the creation of CRHT teams was this perceived failure of services to manage risk adequately.

Managing risk in CRHT teams

CRHT teams have challenged some of the traditional ways of working and have adopted a different approach to service delivery, including:

❖ working in a more collaborative manner with service users;

❖ providing a service in the least restrictive environment as possible for the service user;

❖ adopting a 'gatekeeping' role for people with the potential for hospital admission.

These may prove to be extremely challenging concepts for some. The thought of leaving a person at home while they are experiencing an acute mental health crisis may appear, in some cases, to be somewhat negligent. In addition, working alongside a person in the community who is in crisis may appear a daunting task for practitioners who may not have had the opportunity to experience working in this way.

Positive risk management is about examining and analysing the possibilities available at any given time in any given situation, and being able to support an action that is the 'best' for the service user within that context. This, however, does not mean taking unnecessary risks or being cavalier in approach. It is a way of weighing up the options and being able to make the 'right' choice based on the information available rather than feeling forced into a choice based on previous patterns of care or invalid perceptions of risk. While the literature states that the least restrictive environment should be utilised, this may still mean that an admission to hospital is the right decision and as a consequence should not be seen as a failure on the part of the team.

What do CRHT teams do differently?

People with mental health problems who exhibit the most high-risk behaviour tend to be those who end up being admitted to hospital. As CRHT teams work with those who would otherwise be admitted to hospital, they will be working with people who exhibit risk behaviours and have complex mental health needs. In view of this it is important to identify what characteristics these teams should possess to enable them to manage risk in a community setting. Some of the characteristics outlined below may be shared with other teams, but not in the same context.

Team approach

The team has a shared caseload rather than working with individual cases. Decisions concerning risk are made as a team, wherever possible, with all team members contributing both to the decision and to its implementation. Shared decision making and shared accountability and responsibility go a long way to supporting positive risk taking.

For these characteristics to exist the team should have a forum to discuss risk on a case-by-case basis which, considering the nature of the client group, should take place daily at handover, with more in-depth discussion taking place in extended weekly clinical reviews. This differs from a community mental health team where a community psychiatric nurse (CPN) may make decisions about their caseload in isolation from the rest of the team. This can often lead to defensive practice and risk aversion.

Increased threshold for managing risk

As a consequence of following this team approach, being more easily accessible and being available over a 24-hour period, we would suggest that CRHTs have an increased threshold for managing risk. The management of risk must therefore be seen in the context of the resources available. The fact that where these teams have been effective they have shown significant reductions in hospital admissions suggests this is the case (Minghella *et al.,* 1998). When practitioners within CRHT teams become more confident and competent at dealing with the many risk factors that they face, they become increasingly more able to make sound clinical decisions.

Clarity of role

The team has a clear identity and purpose within the whole system, which supports a consistent approach to decision making. The emphasis on decision making about whether to admit to hospital or not, and the impact that risk has upon this decision, helps the team focus on risk assessment in a way that may not be the case in traditional services.

Multidisciplinary working

Professional differences may occur in any team and this is not necessarily a bad thing. The real danger is if this is allowed to impinge on the package of care delivered to an individual and, worse still, if it compromises risk management. There is value in diversity and teams consisting of many disciplines can have diversity in abundance. While a team can bring together a wealth of experience, both from training and from life experiences, it can also create some differences in methodologies and approaches.

Effective leadership and a commitment to a shared philosophy usually assist in the cohesion of teams. If this is in place then they can reduce the risks significantly. Members of the CRHT team need to be able to trust each other and respect their opinions and experiences in order to enable positive risk management. The role of the team manager/leader is paramount in securing and fostering a culture where staff can practise in a manner that does not inhibit therapeutic, creative and innovative approaches.

Shared values

In order to practise in a fully functioning and effective manner the team must adopt, to some degree, a culture of shared values. When working with service users in distress it is often difficult to remain without judgement and prejudice. The team should develop a culture whereby values can be adopted that suit all the members of staff and meet the objectives of the service. Without this there is a danger of individual practitioners taking unnecessary risks in the community because they have different (not necessarily wrong, but different) values from those of the other members in the team. Having many different values within the team may not be so easy to justify in the case of an incident taking place as a consequence of a practitioner's actions. Although the philosophy of 'team-working' fosters cohesion it needs to be continually evaluated and reviewed in order that some practitioners do not take this as an opportunity to make less of a contribution. This is where there is a need for leadership and development within the team in order to encourage cohesion and a shared philosophy.

Risk can be reduced if the whole team understands and actively subscribes to a philosophy and culture. This in turn can reduce professional boundaries in the workplace.

Providing 24-hour, 7-days-a-week service

The ability to respond over a 24-hour period to crisis is much more likely to promote positive risk taking. Practitioners are aware that when they leave a situation after making an assessment, they can easily return, if necessary, as they are often only a phone call and a short journey away. Where longer distances are the norm, for example in some rural areas, decision making must account for that fact.

Where community services are only provided between 9 am and 5 pm there is often a 'vacuum' out-of-hours, where the only options are to go to the local A&E, the local inpatient unit or organise a Mental Health Act assessment. All of these are for the most part unsatisfactory responses. The likelihood, therefore, if faced with these sparse and limited resources, is that decisions will often err on the side of caution and the most restrictive option will be selected.

Extended time available for assessment and intervention

CRHT teams are resourced to be able to spend longer periods of time with individuals in a community setting. They should provide a more thorough assessment and have the time to provide more intensive intervention to minimise the risks.

Strengths approach

This approach was put forward by Charles Rapp and resonates with the working of CRHT teams (Rapp, 1998). In essence CRHT teams are encouraged to weigh up risk in the context of the individual's strengths rather than focusing solely on the negative aspects of risk. Assessment and intervention therefore have to focus on the individual's protective factors and how they affect the level of risk. A simple example would be where an individual is depressed and vulnerable when they are on their own in the house and they have no motivation to prepare meals, etc. This risk might be countered by the fact their sister is going to stay with them and will take over some of these tasks. We can see in a very different way, and make very different decisions, if we take the time to consider balancing factors and individual strengths. Consequently, the expectation is that working on the individual's strengths can have a positive impact on reducing risks.

Social system focus

Risk has to be considered in the context of the environment and the social systems in which an individual belongs. More often than not the social system is involved in the crisis. The role of the social system in the resolution of the crisis needs to be considered through active involvement at all stages of the team's intervention. Often the social systems can be seen within a strengths approach as a protective factor, so teams need to make every effort to engage them.

What is needed to support effective working on risk?

Ford & Kwakwa (1996) suggest that: "Poorly delivered crisis services can have a detrimental effect on clients and increase their admissions to hospital." In addition to the potential increase in hospital admissions if CRHT is poorly delivered, people who stay at home in a crisis may also face additional risks.

In addition to the organisational issues that affect the management of risk we also need to consider the needs of individuals working in services. Some of the difficulties for staff may be:

❖ not becoming familiar with their own personal threshold for managing risk;

❖ not understanding or appreciating the way in which their colleagues work;

❖ not being comfortable with their role within the team;

❖ not being familiar with the team's philosophy of positive management of risk in the community;

❖ not yet being confident and competent with the risk tools employed by the team and the trust;

❖ a lack of understanding of the fragilities and strengths associated with interdependence between teams within a whole systems approach (e.g., the need to develop effective working relationships with other parts of the system such as the CMHT);

❖ not appreciating that other teams may not understand the role and/or function of the CRHT team or how this confusion may jeopardise initial progress;

❖ not understanding or obtaining the level of organisational and managerial support required for this approach to be fully effective.

Until most, if not all, of these problems are clearly defined or addressed it is difficult to take a positive approach to risk management and develop effective risk management plans.

Other systems will need to be in place to help staff to manage risk effectively. They include the following:

Managerial policy and support

Without such support the team may feel that they are working within a blame culture and feel stifled. This in turn may restrict opportunities for the service user. Policy can also provide the safeguards necessary for practitioners to adopt this approach with increasing confidence.

Agreed decision-making processes

The need for forums to enable team discussion has been mentioned already, but it is equally important that a decision is made following this discussion. There will often be different opinions as to what should happen, but who makes the decision? Strong leadership is essential; being able to listen to the arguments, formulate a decision and then enact that decision through seeking compromise or giving a clear rationale is a skill that team leaders of all professions need to possess.

Quality clinical supervision

This is essential as practitioners need the opportunity to discuss cases and their development. It needs to be offered and delivered in a constructive way for it to be effective and beneficial to practitioners. Because of the nature of CRHT work, the first thing that gets postponed when the workload is high is supervision. Structures need to be put in place to ensure that time is protected and supervision is seen as a high-priority activity.

Training opportunities

Staff in the team may encounter things for the first time in their careers and this may give rise to skills deficits. Training needs to be identified to supplement this. Whole team training may be vital for some issues and individual training for more specific issues that may be apparent following clinical supervision or identified in personal development plans.

Culture

There needs to be a culture of learning as opposed to a culture of failure and blame within the team and the service as a whole.

Agreed crisis and contingency plans

Crisis plans should be commonplace and so should contingency plans. If teams can utilise as much foresight as their experience allows, they can develop ever-improving contingency plans for service users. Being responsive in a calculated manner with some degree of pre-planning can minimise negative or unwanted consequences in a lot of cases.

Prevention focus rather than reactive focus

This should be inherent within the philosophy of the CRHT team, but nevertheless it needs highlighting regularly to maximise the therapeutic interventions being offered. Prevention in the context of CRHT refers to the team's ability to predict crisis at an early stage and act to de-escalate that crisis. The nature and level of the team's input puts them in an excellent position to manage this.

Thorough assessment protocol

Thorough and appropriate assessment tools should be used. Assessment tools other than specific risk tools may also alert practitioners to risk factors and these should not be overlooked. Teams should hold a resource of assessment tools and be able to use them. Teams will usually have a preference for the assessment tools they use while the trust will, usually, dictate the risk assessment tool to be utilised. In conjunction with risk-specific rating scales other standardised assessment tools may help with the assessment and inform the plan. These include global symptom-rating scales, medication side-effect monitoring tools, and quality of life scales.

Personal safety protocols

Owing to the fact that CRHT teams often work over a 24-hour period, account needs to be taken of the personal safety needs of staff. Different protocols will often exist in the day as opposed to the night but, given the nature of the work, this is something that must be taken very seriously at all levels of the organisation. Local solutions should be sought, using all relevant personnel and technology to ensure staff are working in as safe an environment as is possible.

Understanding confidentiality

Confidentiality is an issue across health services and most professional bodies will have guidance on the subject. Sensitivity is required in the case of mental health, in particular for services based in the community. This can be because of the reactions of the local community if people become aware that mental health services are involved with a person. Social exclusion, stigmatisation and victimisation can compound the issues that the team is attempting to address.

In investigations following incidents the degree to which something was kept in confidence can be called into question. Confidentiality should not be seen as an 'absolute' term, in that there will be occasions when information has to be shared in order to maintain the safety of all concerned. Quite often problems can be overcome by a 'common-sense' philosophy and by utilising a 'need to know' approach. There will always be times of uncertainty in this kind of work. The value of the team approach is that concerns about confidentiality can be openly discussed by the team on a daily basis and more often if necessary, and those with the appropriate skills, knowledge and accountability can be actively involved in the decision making.

Conclusion

Risk and its management require a great deal of attention. Risk does not always have to be viewed in a negative manner. It is a vital part of a collaborative approach that can afford the service user the opportunity to develop and maximise their potential. Practitioners working in crisis resolution teams will face situations regarded as 'high risk' by many people on an almost a daily basis. With this in mind there needs to be a philosophy adopted by the team that can foster positive approaches in working with and managing the risks that they and their service users face.

The social systems approach

Chris Bridgett

Introduction

The social systems approach recognises the importance of social relationships in creating and maintaining good mental health. A breakdown in someone's social relationships may trigger or exacerbate a mental health crisis. Practitioners work with everyone involved in a service user's life, from family and friends to colleagues and neighbours, to identify the reasons for the crisis and to find ways to bring about a resolution.

In recent years community mental health services have focused on mental state assessment and medication, rather than on the social aspects of mental health such as the impact of life events and the support networks available. The structured approaches of case management and the care programme approach (DH, 2000b) have led to the increased use of inpatient care (Tyrer *et al.*, 1995) and proposed amendments to the current Mental Health Act may also have a similar effect. Crisis resolution, which focuses on supporting the individual in the community, presents an important counterbalance to these trends.

The antecedents of crisis resolution and home treatment (CRHT) can be found in the therapeutic community approach to providing psychiatric inpatient and day patient care, developed in the 1950s and 1960s (Jones, 1968). For example, the work of Maxwell Jones and Paul Polak at Dingleton Hospital, Scotland, and Denver, USA (Polak, 1970; Polak & Jones, 1973) showed how the established therapeutic effectiveness of working with social relationships in institutional settings could be successfully and appropriately transferred to real-life settings outside hospital.

Today, the relevance of working with the individual and their social circumstances is emphasised in NHS policy implementation guides (DH, 2001a, 2001b, 2001c, 2002b) for all specialist and generic teams.

In everyday practice a focus on social systems is often reduced to the idea of holding a 'social systems meeting', where all the people involved in the crisis are invited to meet and talk through what has happened. Such group work may cause anxiety for practitioners who are used to working on a one-to-one basis, but once the benefits of this way of working are appreciated, such anxiety is quickly replaced by a confident broader view of what can be done in practice.

However, the social systems meeting is only one type of social systems intervention (Bridgett & Polak, 2003b) in what is better described as an overall social systems approach. Rather than having a focus on the individual, the social systems approach considers the importance of social circumstances as fundamental, from referral and assessment through to discharge and follow-up. The approach allows for a wide variety of interventions other than the social systems meeting. It is the purpose of this chapter to bring examples of these together.

CRHT is provided within a crisis intervention framework (see Chapter 1). Crisis intervention is a way of helping people in difficulty that is widely applicable beyond the remit of a home treatment team

(Rosen, 1997). Crisis resolution applies only to those problems that would otherwise require inpatient care. From its beginnings in the preventive work of Gerald Caplan, crisis intervention has worked not only with the individual, but also with the social context of the individual. Indeed, once the idea of how a crisis affects the individual is understood, the way the same characteristics are relevant to the social system is easily appreciated. The principles of crisis intervention are as important for working effectively with social systems as they are for working with the individual.

Basics

Each one of us necessarily relates to other individuals in a variety of ways. The behaviour of one person affects that of others. The way in which the individual parts of any whole have such interactive relationships was formulated in the 1960s as general system theory (von Bertalanffy, 1968). Social systems are two or more interacting people: their relationship may be formal or informal, fixed or transitory. An individual may relate to a number of social systems (see Figure 1), which may be seen as 'domains'. Systems overlap and interact with each other, forming a social network.

General system theory states that a system always seeks equilibrium. When an event such as bereavement, job problems or illness disturbs a social system and it is not able to cope, then a crisis exists in the social system. Because systems can interact, a crisis in one system can lead to a crisis in another and a chain of crises may result (Morrice, 1968). The common origins of such difficulties are the same for social systems as they are for individuals. Crisis theory emphasises that both individuals and social systems are more amenable to help when they are in crisis.

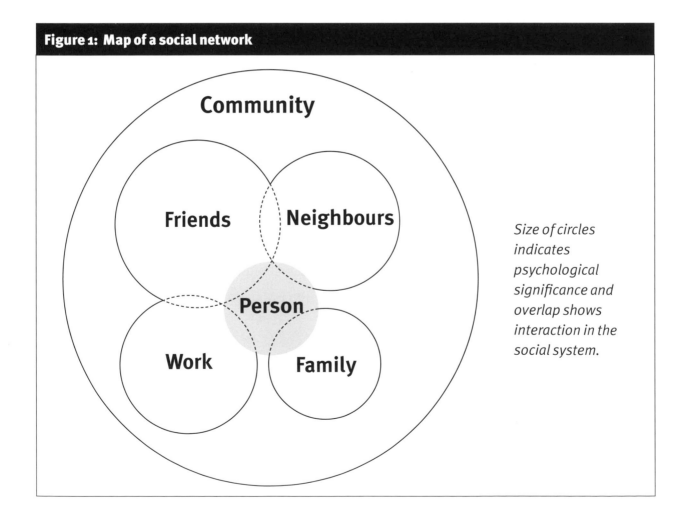

Figure 1: Map of a social network

Community

Friends   Neighbours

Person

Work   Family

Size of circles indicates psychological significance and overlap shows interaction in the social system.

Stressful life events can precipitate and exacerbate episodes of mental illness. The effect on an individual may be both direct and indirect, through its impact on important social relationships. The illness of the individual also represents a stress for a social system. How the system copes with this will depend on its strengths and weaknesses. When events are sufficiently stressful to disturb its equilibrium, one coping strategy can be to sacrifice an individual member in favour of re-establishing equilibrium (see Vignette 3 on 'scapegoating').

Vignette 1 shows a sequence of events that can represent the pathway to inpatient care.

Vignette 1: Single bereaved professional

A single and childless middle-aged professional woman, living alone since the death of her mother two years previously, is brought to A&E by friends from her church who are exhausted by their efforts to help her. She is severely depressed and neglecting herself, and has been 'off sick' for several weeks after an episode of uncharacteristic and inappropriate behaviour at work. The GP is investigating her cardiac function; the CMHT primary care liaison nurse is involved. She has been chronically intoxicated with alcohol since her bereavement. Her older siblings and their families live abroad; they have not been close to her for several years. She seems to have lost touch with her godchildren.

In Vignette 1, there is a need for intensive care initially as an inpatient for detoxification and then at home by the crisis resolution team. This has arisen through a crisis in the woman's social system of close and caring friends. This crisis was preceded by difficulties at work, which began following the death of her mother. Her inability to cope then may be linked with her having been the sole support for her mother for a number of years, as her siblings lived overseas. Thus one crisis is seen to relate to another, through social systems overlapping. The crisis that needs immediate attention by a home treatment team can be termed the 'referral crisis'. It is the problem that needs addressing immediately to stabilise the situation. Such containment has traditionally been the role of the acute admission ward. When admission is necessary, the subsequent negative impact of inpatient care on the service user's social adjustment has been termed the 'crisis of admission' (Polak, 1967).

When discussing what has happened in a particular case, it is useful to represent the various social systems in a diagram or map (Bridgett & Polak, 2003a). Figure 2 shows the social systems of the single bereaved professional described in Vignette 1.

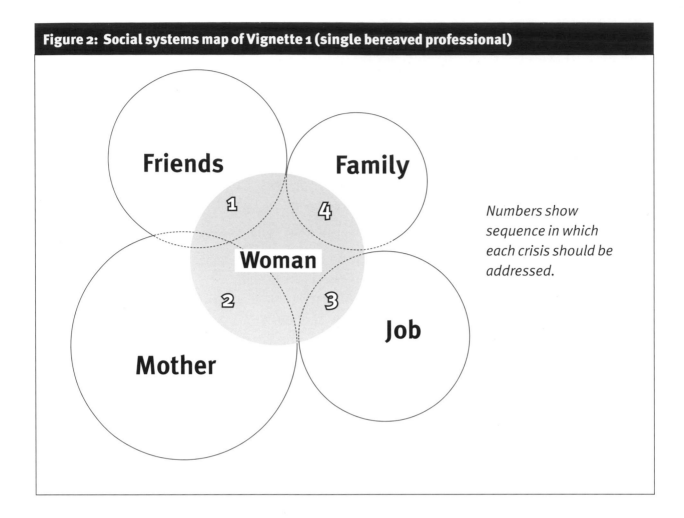

Figure 2: Social systems map of Vignette 1 (single bereaved professional)

Friends

Family

1

4

Woman

2

3

Job

Mother

Numbers show sequence in which each crisis should be addressed.

Such mapping helps the team to understand the social systems and crises relevant to a particular referral. The service user is placed at the centre of the map with interlinking social relationships. The first task to be addressed by the team is the referral crisis caused by her friends' inability to cope. If this is not addressed, then admission to an inpatient ward may be necessary.

The mapping exercise then considers the next social systems crisis to be addressed. In this case, it is not an event that is in chronological sequence. The woman's bereavement seems of greater psychological importance for the home treatment management plan than her more recent difficulties at work.

The apparent lack of support from her family overseas is a more distant issue, but may have contributed to her current predicament. The crisis resolution team first contains the referral crisis, and then promotes healthy grieving. Supporting a return to work and establishing appropriate family support might then be tasks taken on by the relevant community mental health team (CMHT), after discharge from the crisis resolution team.

Beginning

The social systems approach begins when a referral is first made. The operational policy of a service optimally requires the CRHT team to gatekeep (Protheroe & Carroll, 2001) access to the acute ward. This *triage* function can be pivotal in successfully managing a case. All referrals benefit from a comprehensive assessment as soon as possible, whether or not an admission is necessary. With a necessary admission there are still important social issues to investigate and document for future work (see Chapter 5 on facilitating early discharge). The crisis resolution team ideally sits between several elements of a service, all involved in direct patient care. Thus, the gatekeeping of admissions is a social systems intervention, where the systems concerned include the service itself.

The sooner information is gathered, the more likely important social aspects of the crisis can be accurately understood (Sutherby & Szmukler, 1995). As time passes, the heat goes out of a crisis: significant others retreat, new staff become involved, the story is handed over from shift to shift, and the social dimension of the referral is relegated to second place. Thus initial emphasis is usually placed on mental state, on risk assessment, on the need for containment and on medication. This approach often results in the person being admitted to an acute ward. The social systems approach requires further information in order to understand the social circumstances.

Experience shows that the best way to obtain this information is to make an average of three telephone calls (Polak, 1972) to significant others immediately after referral and prior to a lengthy interview with the service user. The phone calls should identify which social systems are involved, which social systems crisis it is practical to tackle first and who should be invited to the first meeting.

The team then has the opportunity to build a comprehensive formulation or hypothetical framework showing causes, effects, interventions and likely results. An initial synopsis can be produced, with the **problems** to be tackled, the **plan of action** to be undertaken and the **people** (key professionals and significant others) to involve. It will serve both as an initial notification to others that a case has been taken on, and provide the team with a memory aid for the work to be carried out.

The first discussions with those involved in a referral provide an opportunity for those conducting the assessment to set the scene for the social systems approach by explaining the relevance of social circumstances. The immediate environment of the first contact may be less than conducive for an adequate and accurate assessment. This should be acknowledged with a suggestion that a home-based assessment could be arranged. Initially, everyone may be preoccupied with coping with the referral crisis: the mental state of the patient, their willingness or otherwise to seek and receive help, and the appropriateness of the service response. An early exploration of the circumstances of the difficulties experienced recently by everyone involved, including colleagues in other teams, allows an explanation of how the crisis resolution team aims to work. Such initial discussion encourages an understanding that the approach is going to be comprehensive, taking into consideration a wide variety of issues.

As the assessment proceeds, it is necessary to identify the agreed crisis origins. When did the difficulties begin? What stressful events occurred prior to that time? Who are the people involved in the life of the person referred, and what events have affected them that have changed things for the person referred?

Continuing care

As the history is accumulated, the plan of care can divide interventions into those that need achieving in the short term, and those that can be left until later.

Vignette 2: 55-year-old man

A 55-year-old man, with a history of schizophrenia well controlled by oral medication, is referred with the story that, having stopped taking his recommended medication, his mental state has recently deteriorated. He is alarming neighbours and others by appearing naked at his front door when visited.

Assessment reveals that he stopped taking his medication soon after his wife's father become seriously ill. Since then his wife had spent much of her time at her parents', and expected her own daughter to continue to support him and ensure that he took his medication. This failed to happen – he was a 'difficult man' and he and his daughter had never got on.

For the service user in Vignette 2, who is known to the mental health service, the previous care plan would be revealed by the care co-ordinator on referral. The visiting home treatment team would then work alongside existing support, ensuring that all understand and agree a revised care plan. Anticipating resolution of the crisis, new support may need to be recruited before discharge is possible. Although this can be achieved without those involved meeting face-to-face, a meeting with the service user in his home with all involved, as soon as possible, is recommended (Bridgett & Polak, 2003b; Polak, 1972; Fish, 1971). This addresses understanding and communication issues and ensures that expectations are realistic.

Facilitating such a meeting is not difficult, if it is remembered that this involves a set of relationships that, although now not coping with difficulties, has been previously in equilibrium. The purpose of the meeting is to enable a return to equilibrium, through discussion and the promotion of healthy coping. Although more than one meeting may prove necessary, if the first meeting is held as soon as possible, with all of the key people present, a great deal can be achieved with one meeting alone. In preparing for the meeting the crisis team should allocate two of its members to act as facilitators, one being more active than the other. Before the meeting a hypothesis about the situation should be agreed, which can then be revised after the meeting. At the meeting it is important to encourage discussion of the 'here and now', rather than a detailed raking-over of past events. Otherwise, the agenda should be allowed to emerge at a natural pace: confrontation with reality and expression of feeling should be encouraged, but any resistance should be allowed to postpone further exploration until those involved feel ready to proceed.

Very easy-to-use techniques that facilitate discussion include reflecting back what has just been said, perhaps emphasising a particular point in a way that asks for elaboration. This can be directed at the person who has spoken, or at one of the listeners. Condensing a long speech into what seems to be the essentials can provoke useful discussion, as can attempting to say the same thing in a different way – rewording.

The emphasis on the 'here and now' is partly to make the meeting immediately relevant in a practical sense, but also aims to steer away from the early introduction of more difficult psychological techniques. The offering of interpretations should only be considered with caution. Sometimes one member of the meeting emerges as the natural spokesperson of the system (such as the example of the parish priest in Box 1) and this may prove useful. In order to enable the contribution of someone who otherwise may remain silent, a 'psychodrama' technique may be helpful: the therapist offers to speak for a silent member, saying "I would like to see if I can speak for you here: tell me if this is wrong ..." As with interpretations, it is important to take account of the expectations of those present before using such a technique.

Box 1: First social systems meeting: single bereaved professional (see Vignette 1)

After an uneventful three-day admission for detox, arranged because of concerns about her cardiac status, the home treatment team organises a meeting for the service user on her first evening at home. This includes her two friends who brought her to A&E and the parish priest, who has known her family for many years. It was anticipated that her friends would confront her with their frustration over her behaviour, and there would be an opportunity to decide on the best way forward.

The priest began, however, by remembering her mother, saying he had taken the liberty of looking around the apartment, and that he could see everything was the same as it had been when her mother was alive. The friends agreed: it was now time for her to move on. They would be happy to visit each day to help sort things out and tidy up, but on condition that they first cleared out all the alcohol and she agreed to remain sober and to attend AA meetings regularly. The priest suggested she should also begin to help again at church.

The crisis team advised that they and her care co-ordinator from the CMHT would arrange daily visits to monitor the situation. They were also keen for her to talk with the team psychologist about her difficulties since her mother died. When she responded by reassuring everyone that she was fine and they really were not to worry, one of the friends sat forward and said:

66 *Look, I have wanted to say this for some time, and now I'm going to say it: we have all had enough of you talking as if you are coping, when you are plainly not. What happened at work? Why were you sent home? Why are you now going to see the heart specialist? What has happened to the neat and tidy person you used to be? You have to stop pretending that nothing has happened, or we will stop coming round and, then goodness knows, what will happen to you.* 99

The silence that followed was broken by the priest:

66 *You are surrounded by very good friends: now is the time to let them help you. I know it would be what your mother would have wanted.* 99

At this she turned to look at a framed photograph of her mother on a side table next to her, and began to cry.

The meeting continued with the friends and the priest remembering with her how she had cared for her mother, especially during her final illness. The meeting ended with an agreement for a further meeting four days later. In the meantime, she agreed to accept the help offered by her friends, and to meet with the psychologist. The crisis team staff reviewed their initial hypothesis, and noted the further evidence gained of unresolved grief.

Working towards resolving a social systems crisis requires a variety of interventions, which can usefully be reviewed in meetings with those concerned, but which do not necessarily need such group discussion. Thus, the co-ordination of involved support, as in a care programme approach meeting, can also be achieved by alerting others by telephone to what has happened and to what seems to be needed.

Initial short-term changes that the home treatment team can consider might include the involvement of additional formal support, when otherwise those involved will fail to cope. Advice on benefits and accommodation may be necessary. Overall the home treatment team is well placed to improve communication and understanding: enabling an appreciation of what is possible, compared with what may be impossible, to facilitate coping.

Crisis intervention is a fruitful way of working, as in crisis both individuals and their social systems are more amenable to change. The home treatment team takes advantage of this as it works towards crisis resolution. Issues which before the crisis may have seemed problematic to deal with now become clearer to address. Thus crisis resolution might allow, and require, useful role and relationship clarification within a family, or group of involved professionals. The latter consideration for service users known to a service can highlight recent weaknesses in available support. Thus a frequent change in key worker is often cited by service users in crisis as an important cause of the failure to cope.

Community survival skills such as self-care, housekeeping, obtaining benefits and finding work are important for coping, and a review of what can be done to improve matters, in both the short and longer term, may be part of crisis resolution work. Although such skills can be discussed on a one-to-one basis, more robust improvements in coping will be achieved if significant others are involved, and when appropriate the care programme approach meeting can be used to highlight what has been agreed.

The arrangement of long-term support, both informal and formal, must go hand-in-hand with the anticipation of future hazards. One most often considered is how both the individual and those around them will first recognise relapse (Birchwood & Drury, 1995) and then, with a failure in coping, manage a future crisis. Crisis cards (Sutherby *et al.,* 1999) should always carry information on the individual's key social supports. Finally, crisis resolution offers a continuing opportunity to review the adequacy of services provided to a local community. If there are regular opportunities to feed back the experiences of a crisis resolution team to service managers and commissioners, valuable indicators for service improvement will be identified.

The crisis resolution team and the ward

Admission for inpatient care may immediately resolve the acute failure in coping (the referral crisis). It can be argued, however, that the social environment of the traditional psychiatric ward has little or no relevance to the disturbances in social context in the real-life setting that brings the service user there. It was previously estimated that the average acute psychiatric admission addressed only one-third of the pertinent issues, largely relating to the individual, that create the need for hospitalisation. Two-thirds, largely relating to social circumstances, remain to cause future difficulties on discharge (Morrice, 1968; Polak, 1967). Despite the developments in community psychiatry since these assertions were made, contemporary clinical experience continues to endorse their relevance.

Optimally, acute care should be closely co-ordinated between the team and the ward (Smyth, 2003). Gatekeeping can generate, in conjunction with the ward, a care plan that includes reference to the social circumstances that need to be addressed. In some cases these can, and should, be dealt with immediately or at least during the inpatient stay. Otherwise, the team and the ward should plan discharge at the time of admission, anticipating that some of the social issues will best be dealt with on or after discharge, in the real-life setting.

Understanding the referral crisis in terms of a failure to cope without the admission to the ward can be especially useful. The need for inpatient care is otherwise too often associated with deterioration in mental state, perhaps linked to a failure to take recommended medication. Such over-reliance on a strictly medical perspective can lead to a delayed discharge caused by a failure to address social factors early. Thus, although inpatient care will always be a necessary part of mental health services, the psychosocial side effects of such care must be taken into account, regarding both the effects on the social systems that the individual will return to and the effects of institutional life on the individual in the meantime.

Labelling, scapegoating and extrusion are social processes that can lead to admission to inpatient care (Polak, 1972). When a social system is affected by a significant life event, it can enter a period of disequilibrium. A vulnerable person within such a system may take the brunt of the disturbance, with the system labelling them as a 'patient'. The 'patient' can then become a scapegoat. The system may re-establish a new equilibrium, by extrusion: the admission of the patient to hospital. It is a phenomenon that needs to be considered at the gatekeeping assessment to avoid inappropriate admissions and delayed discharges (see Vignette 3).

Vignette 3: Scapegoating

A married 40-year-old man with no children is taken one evening by his wife and her relatives from their cramped temporary accommodation in central London to an A&E department in a neighbouring district. He appears to be in a state of 'collapse'. He had been involved in a minor traffic accident one week before and an episode of amnesia the day before. There is also a three-year history of paranoid behaviour associated with a business failure in the north of England.

Six weeks previously he had moved with his wife to work in London. At the A&E department no physical illness is found and, in view of his disturbed behaviour, he is referred immediately to his local mental health centre for assessment, possibly for admission. He arrives on his own for an assessment at 10 pm, his wife and family having gone home, and is admitted to the ward overnight.

An attempt to arrange a family meeting the next day reveals severe tensions, when the family refuses to involve him in their discussion with the crisis resolution team. This prevents immediate continuing care outside hospital. Inpatient care continues for several weeks, during which his wife decides to separate from him. Discharge is delayed because he does not have accommodation to go to.

If in Vignette 3 the crisis resolution team had gone immediately to the A&E department, and assessed the man with his wife and her family before he was transferred, it is possible that the admission to the ward could have been avoided. As it turned out, his wife's family, who had been dismayed from the outset by her marriage to someone they regarded as inherently unstable, used the crisis to force a separation while he was an inpatient.

Closing cases

From assessment onwards, planning future care is essential for effective CRHT: if the social network of the individual is taken into account, such future care is more likely to be successful. Thus, when it is understood that the individual's capacity to cope will be determined significantly by social circumstances, then agreeing to have in place an appropriate set of social supports is crucial to future care (Bridgett & Polak, 2003b; Tyrer *et al.,* 2003). The process of ensuring optimal arrangements involves working with both informal (family and friends) and formal carers, especially the relevant CMHT. For new service users, appropriate future care can be ensured by providing the new CMHT care co-ordinator with a 'needs assessment' that emphasises the relevant social circumstances. With known cases, having the existing CMHT care co-ordinator working alongside the home treatment team will further facilitate appropriate future care.

Discharge arrangements need also to take account of all involved, from the time of initial assessment onwards, if potential problems are to be avoided. Contact with a CRHT team is necessarily measured in days and weeks, rather than months. The intensity of this contact with both the individual and their significant others is such that it is not likely to be replicated by subsequent care arrangements on follow-up. If the time-limited nature of this input is not appreciated from the start by those benefiting from it, discharge and transfer on to care by colleagues can be unwelcome and problematic. On discharge it is usual to offer future crisis help, should the need arise. This should be offered jointly to the individual and to their informal carers. A crisis plan can usefully make arrangements explicit, as part of the care programme approach.

Training in the social systems approach

Probably the most effective type of training using social systems interventions is 'on the job'. This can be organised at different levels of intensity. For example, new teams can benefit from enlisting the involvement of an external consultant to work alongside the team for a week at a time; joining in at all stages of care to show how to incorporate the social systems approach successfully. Such training can usefully be repeated at intervals – perhaps once or twice a year – to build up expertise, and provide training for newcomers. On a more regular basis, perhaps weekly, it is useful to provide an opportunity for the team to present cases from the social systems point of view, with an appropriately trained external moderator facilitating the discussion. Such group supervision will often provide an opportunity to look at not only the social dynamics of the service users being cared for by the team, but also the dynamics of the service – how the team experiences working within the organisation of which it is necessarily a part.

More theoretical training can include a variety of multidisciplinary workshop exercises, as well as teaching on specific topics arranged within a team on a rota basis.

Audit of outcomes can provide a useful opportunity for reflective practice, if the team agrees to enter a social prognosis in the closing summary of all cases. Thus, the summary can detail on discharge the team's assessment of how the person will cope in the future, and what social factors will be important for success, and failure. Six or twelve months later, cases can be reviewed with others involved, enabling the team to better understand long-term outcomes in terms of the social systems approach.

Conclusion

Crisis resolution and home treatment provides important new opportunities in acute psychiatric care that the traditional acute ward rarely, if ever, provides. Simply transferring care from the ward to the home improves matters significantly, as social context has a powerful effect on behaviour – something often completely overlooked when assessment and treatment are carried out in an institutional setting. Such care by 'a ward on wheels' will, however, as on the ward, focus on the individual. Crisis intervention requires assessment and treatment to take account of social systems as well. Central to this work is the convening and facilitation of social systems meetings. These are essentially a setting for a wide variety of social systems interventions summarised in this chapter. They are best seen as an overall approach, informing practice from initial referral through to audit at follow-up.

Facilitating early discharge

Nina Lakhani

Introduction

Among the key expectations explicitly identified in the NHS Plan (DH, 2000a) is that CRHT teams will reduce inpatient bed usage by around 30%. This is one reason why facilitating early discharge from hospital is so important: the anticipated reductions are unlikely to come from reducing admissions only. Yet it appears that many CRHT teams have yet to establish an early discharge role for themselves and that there is much variation on how and to what extent this is done.

Experience suggests that this variation causes considerable debate and sometimes conflict within mental health systems. Newly developed and established teams, therefore, are often struggling to achieve model fidelity (i.e. to fit the requirements of government guidance) in this crucial area which frequently, although not inevitably, affects outcomes such as bed usage and service user and carer satisfaction.

This chapter uses examples to illustrate the importance of the early discharge function of a CRHT team, in order to identify ways in which the aims of the team can be fully achieved.

Why is early discharge important?

Studies carried out in the 1950s and 1960s suggested that prolonged care within psychiatric inpatient units can lead to a process of institutionalisation, manifesting itself in the individual's loss of role in the family and in wider society and in their adoption of a 'sick role' (Barton, 1976). This has been supported in more recent studies carried out in inpatient units which suggest that they are not experienced as therapeutic places (SCMH, 1998).

By preventing lengthy admissions and working proactively towards discharge some, if not all, of these adverse consequences can be prevented. The adult acute inpatient policy implementation guidelines describe the purpose of an acute inpatient unit as being to provide a high standard of care and treatment for those service users in the most acute and vulnerable stage of their illness, who cannot at that time be treated appropriately at home or in a less restrictive setting (DH, 2002a). The implementation of CRHT teams is partly to enable inpatient services to have the resources to do this, and is closely related to the nationwide trend of over-full busy acute inpatient units, high bed occupancy rates and increasing use of out-of-area or private sector beds (Garcia *et al.,* 2005). In some areas this process is referred to as extra-contractual referrals (ECRs) and in others as out-of-area treatments (OATs). In reality this means that inpatient staff and service managers are often constantly struggling to find beds for people with acute mental health difficulties. It often means sending someone else home from the ward on leave as they may be seen as 'less unwell'. Service users on occasion have to move several times during their crisis. Disruption to their recovery and delays in their discharge home are inevitable.

Vignette 1: Mr J

Mr J is a 63-year-old man with a long history of serious mental illness who had been admitted to an acute ward after a breakdown in his social network. His care co-ordinator had recently left and the staff in his accommodation were struggling with his ongoing poor self-care. He is a quiet, undemanding man who during this eight-week admission spent time in three different hospitals, two of them private. On both of these occasions, more acutely unwell service users with disruptive behaviour had required admission; hence room was made for them by transferring Mr J, who was described as relatively 'uncomplicated'. However, this meant that his reason for admission was repeatedly lost and not addressed, undoubtedly increasing the time he remained in hospital as well as increasing the pressure on the inpatient unit.

Another implication of this pressure on beds is that admissions can be delayed for hours or even days at a time, leaving service users, carers and staff, who may all feel admission is necessary, feeling frustrated or even unsafe. Vignettes 1 and 2 give examples of the impact of this problem on two hypothetical individuals.

Vignette 2: Mrs H

Mrs H is a 32-year-old woman who was five months pregnant when she was referred to a fully gatekeeping CRHT team. She was experiencing an atypical depressive episode which was difficult to treat and after three weeks of working with her and her family, her safety and that of her baby became a more immediate concern and therefore admission was identified as the necessary intervention. Her family were extremely reluctant and became increasingly angry once the team arrived at the inpatient unit and discovered there was actually no bed in her sector ward. She was instead admitted to a much larger, more chaotic, ward and her medical team changed as a result. She then had to wait for nearly three hours in the day room before she was allocated a bed. The CRHT team were faced with the understandable fury and distress of her family who had been opposed to admission in the first place.

Despite the explicit aims of CRHT teams, pressure on inpatient beds and delayed discharges may remain common occurrences even when admission rates have been reduced following their introduction. There may be less pressure to discharge people and beds may become filled with people with more complex needs (Garcia *et al.*, 2005). Consequently we know of teams who have significantly reduced admission rates, but bed use has remained the same or has even increased.

Inpatient staff may be left facing the same bed management struggles as always, constantly responding to crises and still with little time to focus on care and recovery. As in the example of Mr J, this can occur even if the CRHT team is gatekeeping all admissions and having a positive impact on admission rates, if there is no unified approach to discharge. People like Mr J may remain in hospital because there is no time to deal with the actual crisis leading to admission. Losing the actual reasons for admission can mean that the help the person needs is unclear and that discharge home is unnecessarily delayed.

In addition, if someone has been admitted to a different hospital, for example, it may be far more difficult for people, including the care co-ordinator, to visit because of the distance involved, transport difficulties, communication barriers and lack of integration across trusts. Service users may become 'out of sight and out of mind' until they are ready for discharge and the window of opportunity to work with the social system may be lost (Polak, 1967; Bridgett & Polak, 2003b).

The role of CRHT teams in early discharge

Following a CRHT team assessment, a person in crisis may be immediately admitted to hospital. The person may be known or new to mental health services. The reasons for admission may well be to do with immediate risks and insufficient community support at this stage, and although the CRHT team may not know the service user very well, they should be clear about why they are unable to offer home treatment at this point. They are therefore in a good position to offer this insight to the inpatient team, in order to ensure that valuable information is not lost on admission. Thus a 'good handover' in itself could enable the interventions on the ward to be more focused and relevant as well as facilitating immediate thoughts about the discharge process.

Alternatively, admission may have occurred after a period of input with the service user and therefore it may be important for the CRHT team to maintain the therapeutic relationships with the individual and their social system while they are an inpatient. They might even help to repair these relationships, which are often fraught at the point of admission. Vignette 3 shows how this can work well in practice.

Vignette 3: Mr D

Mr D is a 24-year-old man experiencing a second episode of psychosis with whom the CRHT team had been working for nearly two weeks. During this period his drug use had remained chaotic and his mother and younger sister were finding it difficult to cope with his agitation and poor sleep despite intensive treatment and support by the team. It was therefore agreed to admit Mr D so that these particular issues could be addressed and his family could gain some respite and support. Mr D was initially quite angry and his family felt very guilty. However, all were reassured that the CRHT team would continue to support them and facilitate discharge as soon as possible.

A member of the team and his care co-ordinator were present at the first ward round after admission. Thus there was a familiar face present and reasons for his admission were made clear: that he had not been admitted because of his paranoid thoughts, but rather because of his poor sleep and agitation and the consequences of this on his social system.

The team were able to facilitate leave after a week and discharge in less than two weeks, because the therapeutic relationships and focus for admission had been maintained. The trauma of admission was also minimised for Mr D and his social system, and they were helped to cope more effectively with his illness and the changes to all their relationships.

It is possible that if the CRHT team had not been involved after admission, the social systems focus may have been lost and replaced with the more usual individual symptom-led model of psychiatry, which would have been confusing for Mr D and his family.

Identifying reasons for admission

If the gatekeeping function of the CRHT team is being adhered to then the team should be aware of every inpatient, having participated in the assessment that led to admission. The team should know why each person had been admitted and why home treatment had not been possible at the time. However, in practice, by the time the service user arrives at an inpatient unit and is seen by the duty doctor and nurse for admission, the actual reasons for admission may no longer be clear. A significant amount of time may have passed since the initial assessment when admission was agreed, the handover information may be lost owing to shift changes, and the service user may be more distressed or may have received medication resulting in their sedation. Significant others who were essential in understanding the whole story may no longer be around and thus inevitably a more individual, symptom-focused approach will be adopted and the social reasons for admission marginalised. The focus for admission becomes framed around illness and symptoms, and staff may be apprehensive about discharging an individual who is not 'symptom free'.

Concerns about early discharge may also be raised by families and carers, or even service users, who may be used to lengthier admissions. Furthermore, there are often practical and social issues that can prevent someone from being discharged and, despite being integral to the reasons for admission, these may not have been tackled after several days or weeks of the person being an inpatient (see Vignette 4).

Vignette 4: Miss P
Miss P was admitted to an inpatient ward after her neighbour had complained several times about her loud music at night and had eventually called the police after an altercation that had left Miss P locked out of her flat. After three weeks in hospital she was less distressed and sleeping better, and was referred to the CRHT team by her psychiatrist. At this point, however, Miss P still did not have her flat keys and nor had anybody spoken with her neighbour since her admission. Two of the main triggers for the admission had not been dealt with at all: the reasons for admission had been lost.

While responsibility for identifying and addressing the reasons for admission may lie with all those involved in the assessment, the CRHT team should be consistently involved in this process. The team can then ensure that the reasons for admission are easily documented and also shared by all relevant parties. This can enable joint decisions to be made (i.e., between the consultant, inpatient nurses and care co-ordinator) at the point of admission on what has to change before discharge and who will be tackling each issue.

CRHT team members must therefore be very clear about their reasons for admitting somebody, which helps to cultivate consistency within the service. It would also help to explain the reasons why someone should remain an inpatient and guide discussions in future review meetings. Thus when a referral comes from the ward, the CRHT team can clarify whether the issues identified at the point of admission have been tackled. Discussions may be diverted away from symptoms as the CRHT team is able to work with someone who remains acutely unwell, if the reasons for admission, which are often practical or related to changes in their social system, have been addressed.

Figure 1: Sample early discharge sheet

Crisis resolution home treatment team:

Tel:		Fax:	
Name	Miss P		
D.O.B.	15.06.67		
Date of admission	19.08.06		
Place of admission	Ward 6		
Consultant	Dr Hill		
Care co-ordinator	J. Keegan		
Significant others	John (Neighbour) on 020 82*** 82 Helen (Cousin)		
CRHT review date	24.08.06		

CRHT reasons for admission to hospital:

1) Severe breakdown in her relationship with her neighbour due to loud music being played by Miss P at night.
2) Poor sleep and increased distress due to increased frequency and intensity of hearing derogatory voices.
3) Locked out of her flat and vulnerable due to time of crisis at night.

What needs to change before home treatment can be reconsidered:

1) Liaison with neighbour a.s.a.p., with a face-to-face meeting to be facilitated by care co-ordinator and/or ward staff.
2) Address and treat cause of current mental distress and poor sleep pattern (ward staff).
3) Ensure house keys are obtained – to be arranged by care co-ordinator.

CRHT Assessor: Nina Lakhani

FAX to:

WARD:	CMHT:	CONSULTANT:

The processes described here ensure that all parts of the mental health service, the service user and their significant others are fully involved in all stages of care. This helps to ensure that the length of stay is minimal and the aims of the inpatient care are clear for everybody. Moreover, review dates can be set on the basis of individual clinical and social needs, rather than the needs of the service, which can on occasion delay discharge decisions for several days or even longer. Decisions about discharge are shared by the whole system and focus on the actual reasons for admission.

The sample early discharge sheet (Figure 1) is an example of how this process can be documented. It shows a completed form for the case of Miss P.

How to focus on early discharge

There are a number of underlying principles, as well as practical measures, that are important when developing the early discharge function of a CRHT team. These include the following:

Monitoring trends

For those teams that do not fully gatekeep acute admissions, close working with the inpatient units and a considered approach to early discharge may help tighten up this role. It is essential to know who is being admitted to, and discharged from, the wards, and how these admissions are being initiated so that any gaps in the care pathway can be identified. Cohesive working with the inpatient units and the bed manager is essential for the collection of relevant data; only then will accurate monitoring be possible. Moreover, clarifying how the bed manager can be involved in data collection may be a valuable resource to the CRHT team manager. Baseline data is crucial if services are able to monitor changes in admission rates, average lengths of stay and variations between sectors. The template in Figure 2 may assist those responsible for gathering this information daily, while Box 1 lists the variety of data that may be of interest to services for tracking the early discharge function. Trusts should review bed occupancy levels and use their length-of-stay figures as one method of evaluating the impact of CRHT teams (Garcia *et al.,* 2005).

Box 1: Data required to track early discharge

❖ number of admissions: by consultant/sector

❖ average length of stay: by consultant

❖ number of referrals from the inpatient units: by consultant/sector

❖ number of these referrals accepted for early discharge

❖ early discharge cases – proportion of CRHT team workload.

Working within the whole system

While official guidance states that "if hospitalisation is necessary, [the CRHT team should] be actively involved in facilitating early discharge to minimise the disruption to people's lives" (DH, 2001a), this process often requires the input of many others, for example:

❖ inpatient staff
❖ consultant

Figure 2: A template for admissions data collection

MONTHLY ADMISSIONS　　**Date:**

Date and Time	Name	D.O.B	Consultant/ sector	Source of admission	CRHT involved (Y/N)	Date of discharge or leave

❖ care co-ordinator (from either community mental health, assertive outreach or early intervention team)
❖ service user
❖ family
❖ friends
❖ advocate
❖ supported accommodation staff.

Good liaison and understanding between the CRHT team, care co-ordinators and inpatient units is particularly imperative if the focus of admission is to be maintained. A clear understanding of each other's roles and responsibilities is vital if service users are to remain in hospital only for as long as is absolutely necessary. It may be useful for representatives from the whole service to 'work through' these issues, perhaps creating an agreed admission and discharge policy. In our experience the timing and appropriateness of referrals in particular need to be made explicit.

Joint working at these different interfaces can also be very useful. In one locality, an inpatient unit and a CRHT team were having ongoing difficulties working together and the relationship between the two teams was becoming increasingly fraught. The CRHT team felt they were receiving repeated "inappropriate referrals" from the inpatient unit and the unit felt that the CRHT team "never accepted anyone" for early discharge. An initial meeting was held to clarify that only those who "would otherwise remain in hospital" were suitable candidates for home treatment, as the CRHT team's role was to facilitate early discharge, not every discharge. In addition, the ward was encouraged to refer more proactively, by regularly liaising with the team to discuss potential candidates for early discharge, rather than waiting for ward round decisions or 'bed crisis' situations. This gave some control of the discharge process to the inpatient nurses.

It was then agreed that all referrals that were accepted by the CRHT team from the ward would be jointly assessed with an inpatient team member, to enhance continuity of care for the service user and as an ongoing learning process. Inappropriate referrals and those not accepted by the CRHT team were also fed back to enhance joint working, case by case and at ward rounds and team meetings if necessary.

Embracing new ways of working

The crucial role of the care co-ordinator is highlighted during the admission and discharge process, as many issues and changes still require their lead. Although CRHT team attendance at ward rounds and CMHT meetings is a good starting point, these joint working relationships necessitate a more creative and service user focused approach, which may similarly be best achieved on a 'case-by-case' basis after a more general guiding process has been jointly agreed.

Developing effective ways of working together is of paramount importance if service users are not to be compromised as a result of internal wrangles and differences of opinion. In the service described here, it was agreed that if a person's discharge is delayed due to the absence of a care co-ordinator or psychiatrist and if they meet the criteria for CRHT team input, then it is possible for the discharge care programme approach (CPA) meeting to take place in the community while the service user is under the care of the CRHT team, thus transferring the care from one acute team (inpatient) to another (CRHT). This meant that CPA planning meetings could be held to meet the needs of the service user, and discharge from the ward would not be delayed because of staff absences.

There is of course a particular need for psychiatrists to be involved in the early discharge process as they remain central to both the admission and the discharge decision, especially if the service user has been compulsorily detained. The care co-ordinator position is of course fundamental, and there needs to be ongoing attention to these roles as new ways of working become established (DH, 2005). Moves towards more person-centred care that is delivered collaboratively would facilitate the process of effective crisis resolution. This would embrace the early discharge of service users by being proactive rather than providing reactive services that only consider discharge at weekly ward reviews or when there is a bed crisis. Reviews would instead be determined by service users' needs.

Service models for early discharge

The two models shown here illustrate different ways of working to facilitate early discharge. Effective communication and shared goals between the various parts of the mental health service are essential in this process. It is important to ensure that the reasons for admission are addressed.

Service Model 1 – The simple 'patch-based' model

This model is suitable for services where a consultant psychiatrist retains medical responsibility for the service user in all parts of the mental health service (CMHT, inpatient unit and CRHT team) and the 'patch' covered by the CRHT team is relatively small, with only one to three consultants. It is essential that:

❖ There is regular attendance at ward rounds and CMHT meetings by a member of the CRHT team to review weekly potential candidates for early discharge.

❖ Shift co-ordinators allocate these meetings to team members as part of each day's work.

❖ Consultants facilitate or participate in these weekly clinical reviews in the ward and CMHT, but decisions about discharges are shared and regularly checked by the whole mental health system.

❖ There is joint planning with the ward, CMHT and families/carers to ensure that potential candidates for early discharge are reviewed in an agreed time slot. This can be helpful as it may be uneconomical for team members to attend for the whole ward round.

❖ The CRHT team can re-assess service users prior to the ward round and decide if they need to attend for a particular service user. Ideally there should have been close liaison with ward staff since admission and a thorough understanding of the reasons for admission.

❖ There is consistent attendance by the CRHT team at reviews. This promotes joint working, better inter-team relationships, role modelling, continuation of social systems interventions and an understanding of the CRHT team's role.

This model works best in services where there is 'sectorisation' of wards and service users under the care of a designated consultant, CMHT and CRHT team are admitted to the same ward. It is far easier to remain consistent and plan ahead if service users can readily access their usual mental health professionals. It is harder to use this model if service users are routinely admitted to different wards with different treatment teams, depending on where there is an empty bed. This is because attending ward rounds and review meetings becomes far more time consuming for the CRHT team and it is difficult to plan for each day.

Service Model 2 – The designated early discharge worker model

In this model, the team allocates one member each week to take responsibility for early discharge arrangements. This way of working is suitable for CRHT teams covering a larger geographical 'patch' which may include several CMHTs and patch-based or specialist consultants. The CRHT team is also likely to have its own designated consultant psychiatrist and there is often no continuity in medical care. Such teams will have a greater number of weekly ward and CMHT review meetings to attend which can be difficult to manage within their daily workload.

The designated worker co-ordinates the early discharge function of team, to ensure that all relevant CMHT meetings and ward reviews are attended, service users in out-of-area or private sector beds are followed up and recently admitted individuals are tracked for their progress. The worker may also attend bed management meetings as part of this role.

A number of principles need to be applied:

❖ The designated worker may allocate some of this work to other team members, but retains responsibility for overall organisation.

❖ Other team duties are not the responsibility of this worker during the week, which ensures that an ongoing priority is given to this role.

❖ Other parts of the mental health service such as the inpatient unit, psychiatrists, CMHTs, etc. are informed each week of the designated team member, who is now more able to forge good links with other mental health staff.

❖ Decisions about suitability for early discharge should always include the whole system, so part of this role may include working closely with other professionals or family members to facilitate decision making.

❖ Liaison with wards to identify potential candidates for early discharge will enable the CRHT team to consider each case before the review. It is important to focus on whether the reasons for admission have been addressed.

❖ A consistent agreed approach with wards and care co-ordinators is essential. The system should not depend on who the designated worker is each week.

Conclusion

There are a variety of reasons that are commonly cited for not discharging service users from inpatient care. These include:

❖ Adequate community support is not in place.

❖ Family/social network is reluctant.

❖ The service user does not want to be discharged.

❖ Social reasons are preventing discharge; for example, keys may be lost, the house/flat might be uninhabitable, and there may be no amenities because of unpaid bills.

❖ The person remains symptomatic.

❖ The staff are unclear what the level of risk will be when the service user is discharged.

❖ The staff believe the service user is unlikely to take their medication after discharge.

❖ There is a need to try temporary leave from the ward first.

❖ The service user is waiting to be reviewed by the ward round and/or consultant.

All of these reasons together contribute to unsustainable pressure on inpatient services. Facilitating early discharge for people who have been admitted to an inpatient ward during a mental health crisis has been now defined as a core function of the CRHT team (DH, 2001a). While there are a number of potential barriers to implementing this role, the desirable impact on the lives of service users and on acute inpatient services is considerable.

Our experience shows that results are best when an integrated approach with the whole system is adopted, and agreements about roles and responsibilities clarified early on. Furthermore, as gatekeeper to the acute services, the CRHT team is in an ideal position consistently to identify the reasons for admission, so that there is clarity about its purpose for all those involved, most importantly the service user and their social systems. The focus of admission can then be maintained and the CRHT team be used to facilitate early discharge most effectively.

Working through a crisis: the process of crisis resolution

Patrick McGlynn and Martin Flowers

In this chapter, we use a case study to work through a typical crisis resolution scenario from assessment to resolution, identifying the potential issues that may arise at each stage and the ways in which these may be managed. The solutions offered are not necessarily ideal in every situation but show examples of what has been helpful in a number of teams. They are based on our experiences as practitioners and managers working within teams, and on our work in providing training and service development to teams nationwide. It is essential that CRHT teams work as an integrated part of the 'whole system of mental health care' and we highlight strategies to ensure that this happens throughout the chapter.

The process

The process of CRHT draws on common problem-solving approaches to enable teams to develop a systematic way of targeting their activity. There are four stages in the process of crisis resolution:

❖ **Assessment** – accepting the referral and assessing the crisis. Identifying the contributory factors, the modifying factors and the strengths which might help the individual to resolve the crisis, and finding out who is involved in the crisis.

❖ **Planning** – to develop strategies for managing the crisis in the community setting. This draws on the range of professional and personal skills available in the team.

❖ **Intervention** – carrying out the intervention.

❖ **Resolution** – identifying when the crisis is resolved to a level where the individual no longer requires intensive support from the team, and identifying the tasks that should be completed prior to transfer of care.

This is not a linear process. Indeed at a single point in an individual's care all aspects of this process may be active. It is also important to note the inter-dependence of each of these stages. For example, if the assessment is inaccurate, the planning and intervention are very likely to be ineffective.

Vignette 1 shows an example of a referral to a CRHT team.

Vignette 1: Crisis referral information for Ms G
Referral was made by a GP at 9.30 am requesting assessment for admission to hospital. The GP had been called out after reports that Ms G had run down the street naked in the middle of the previous night. The police were involved at that stage but Ms G had calmed down after they had arrived at the scene.

Ms G is a woman of 33 years. At the time, she was staying with a friend locally because she was afraid of going back to her flat. She had two children aged five and seven years who were also staying at her friend's.

GP described the following presentation:

❖ over-talkative

❖ flight of ideas – moving from one idea to the next with no recognisable link between the two

❖ describes paranoid ideas

❖ pacing around and unable to sit still for any period of time

❖ unable to concentrate

❖ has not slept for two days

❖ poor diet.

The friend had called out the GP because she was concerned about Ms G's behaviour and the effect it was having on her children. |

Phase 1: Assessment

The referral of Ms G highlights a number of important questions which need to be answered in order to move through the crisis resolution process.

Should the referral be accepted?

The referral information given is the beginning of the assessment process, and acceptance will ultimately depend on the criteria that the team use for assessment, i.e., their target population.

The Mental Health Policy Implementation Guide (DH, 2001a) gives a range of exclusion criteria but makes it clear that these are not blanket exclusions. Exclusion based on a person's diagnosis does not recognise the level of need the individual might have and can lead to certain groups being excluded from a service which ultimately could make a difference to their care. CRHT teams have been established to offer an alternative to hospital admission and therefore the team should focus on those who would otherwise be admitted to hospital, many of whom may not have severe mental health problems. CRHT teams appear to be most effective in reducing hospital bed usage where they have adopted an approach of targeting those who would otherwise be admitted to hospital.

If the team is unclear about its referral criteria, it will be difficult for practitioners within the team to know who they should accept and who they should not. It also highlights the potential difficulty for referrers in knowing who they should and should not refer to the team.

Is there enough information to make a decision as to acceptance?

When receiving referrals, teams need to decide what information is required. This raises the question of who takes the referral, should it be clinical or administrative staff, and how should it be documented? Clinical staff may be better placed to take referrals in that they are more familiar with the right questions to ask. It is recommended that teams develop a referral form to capture the information that they consider to be essential for assessing whether a referral is appropriate. This helps in developing consistency in both information gathering and decision making.

It is important that whoever takes the referral phone call obtains as much relevant information as possible. Failure to do this may mean that the referrer has to be contacted again and this may delay the assessment.

Does the team have timely access to information?

This is particularly an issue in a 24-hour service where out-of-hours access to information is often very poor and can inhibit the functioning of the team.

In the case of Ms G, the referral information is adequate and gives some idea of the severity of the crisis. She appears to be at risk of hospital admission and therefore meets the criteria for assessment. Information from local services suggests that she has had no previous contact with psychiatric services. The next step therefore is to set up the assessment.

Cold calling or pre-arranged assessment?

It is always preferable to pre-arrange the visit with the person in crisis and, where possible, members of their social network. It ensures that the visit is at a time convenient to the service user and their social network and gives the practitioner an opportunity to get an up-to-date picture of the situation.

Are staff available to attend for assessment within the hour if necessary?

Given the nature of crisis work, there will always be peaks and troughs in the workload of CRHT teams. Bearing in mind that each assessment can take a significant amount of time (two to four hours in many cases), it is essential that teams work only with their specific target population (i.e., those at risk of being admitted to hospital), otherwise they will spend the majority of their time doing assessments and be unable to provide intensive intervention. The other important issue here is how the team can provide a multidisciplinary response at short notice. The value of this in broadening the scope of the assessment and the provision of a range of crisis interventions is clear, but it must be acknowledged that the introduction of CRHT teams has meant a change in working practices for many professional groups.

What should the team look for in the assessment?

The aim of the assessment is to develop a plan of care. The first step is to make a decision as to whether the individual could be treated at home or whether admission to hospital is necessary. There are a number of key questions that the team should address:

❖ What is the crisis?

❖ Is it a crisis?

❖ What is the level of input required?

❖ What are the views of the family/carer?

❖ Does the team have the appropriate skills?

❖ Have there been attempts in the past to support the individual at home?

❖ Is there a more appropriate service?

❖ What are the relative benefits of a range of venues (e.g., hospital admission or home treatment)?

Defining the crisis is essential as this will be the initial focus of the intervention. In the majority of cases the crisis is defined not in terms of the individual's mental health problem but by identifying the social context of the crisis. In the case of Ms G, the crisis has not been identified by the individual herself, but by her friend and it could be argued that this is a crisis for the friend and the children as well. It is therefore important to question who has the crisis and why is it occurring now? Social systems intervention is discussed in detail in Chapter 4, but it is important to note that all mental health crises have a social context and that often this context is not identified or acted on within acute inpatient settings.

In Ms G's assessment, time was spent with Ms G's friend and her children identifying where they fitted into the crisis. An early decision had to be made as to whether this was a crisis that required acute intervention. Thus the importance of the practitioners carrying out the assessment being clear about the acceptance criteria for the team cannot be overestimated. Where an individual does not meet the criteria for the team, it is also important that the team then identifies more appropriate services for them. Most commonly this may relate to alcohol abuse, where the individual is undoubtedly in a mental health crisis but it may be better managed within specialist alcohol services.

Where acute intervention is indicated, decisions as to where this takes place will depend on the resources available to the team. An estimate has to be made as to the level of input which will be required to manage the crisis in a safe and effective manner. Often this can be a short-term estimate – over the next 24 hours, for example. This is where fidelity to the model of crisis resolution can affect the decision-making process. In the case of Ms G, if the service was unable to respond over a 24-hour period it might not be viable to offer home treatment because the team would not be able to respond when the service was unavailable. Therefore it could be viewed as unsafe and would place an unfair burden on her friend, who would have been unlikely to accept home treatment if it was offered in this way. If things deteriorated overnight, the friend's options would be to get the police involved again or to take Ms G to the local A&E department.

Mental health services often rely on the support and co-operation of carers and at the assessment stage it is important to clarify what their view of the crisis is, the implications of the crisis for them and how they might be involved in resolving it. From the limited research evidence available both nationally and internationally, it appears that there is a high level of support from carers for these services and no study has found that CRHT increases the burden on families (Hoult, 1986; Dean *et al.*, 1993). Ms G's friend appeared to be the key person at the time of assessment and was willing to work with the team to prevent Ms G from being admitted to hospital. In gathering information at the initial assessment the team could identify family members who could have a part to play in Ms G's recovery.

The interventions a team is going to be able to provide will be contingent on the skills available in the team. It is important for CRHT to utilise the skills of the multidisciplinary team but also to consider individual skills, that fall outside the professional role such as hobbies or alternative training that team members may have. A skills audit is a good way of identifying individual skills in the team. Recruitment should offer the flexibility to bring specific skills into the team. Many crisis teams will work with a significant number of people with a dual diagnosis, for example, and where this relates to alcohol abuse it may be important to have the skills to work with this within the team.

Establishing whether the person has received home treatment before will also guide the plan. A number of scenarios may exist. The team may have previously worked successfully with an individual, and they should identify what worked well on that occasion. Would it be appropriate to try something similar if the presentation is similar? The team may have been unsuccessful in working with the individual at home previously, in which case why did it not work? Maybe the team should try something different this time?

After the practitioners have weighed up the relative benefits of the range of options they have at their disposal, they will need to decide on the venue for treatment or intervention. The most usual options would be hospital admission, CRHT intervention or respite with the support of the CRHT team.

To admit Ms G to hospital would potentially have a negative impact on her relationship with her children, although it could be argued that by her remaining at home her relationship with her children was also going to be affected. By assessing the risk associated with this the team concluded:

❖ Admission to hospital may reduce the concern as to the immediate risk to the children but may not be a positive experience for Ms G and her children. The team explored the possibility of using members of the social system to support Ms G in caring for the children. If the children were out of the home environment with other family members for a period of time, the perception of risk would undoubtedly change.

❖ Hospital admission would offer the availability of 24-hour nursing care but was this necessary? With a supportive friend, and potentially family involvement, informal support could be provided in the home. The CRHT team would be able to spend significant periods of time with Ms G during the day and overnight they would be on call to respond to any crisis experienced by Ms G, her friend or her family.

❖ The decision to work with Ms G at home could be reviewed on each visit and if the situation deteriorated the team would be in a position to change that decision if necessary.

❖ No specific treatment option depended on Ms G being in hospital. In reality there is little that can be provided in hospital that cannot be provided for the individual at home. Through discussion with many services nationally, we have identified relatively few characteristics that may be unique to each venue. Box 1 lists some of the comparative benefits of treatment at hospital and at home.

Box 1: Hospital v Home	
Hospital	**Home**
❖ Opportunity to control environment to ensure service user is in a safe environment ❖ Immediate availability of 24-hour nursing care ❖ Perceived reduction in risk	❖ Maintains social system ❖ More direct family involvement ❖ Less institutionalisation ❖ More acceptable to most service users and carers ❖ Less intrusive/traumatic

The main difference between a CRHT assessment and one from a traditional service can be best demonstrated by the ethos that each espouses. CRHT teams should attend each assessment with the expectation that the person will be treated at home, and only when it is clear that this is not a viable option will hospital admission be considered. Traditionally this may not have been the case. Decisions about hospital admission were often made prior to carrying out the assessment. It is not hard to see why this may have been the case in that most resources were based in the hospital setting with community alternatives focusing on community mental health teams (CMHTs), which were not set up to provide intensive acute interventions. If there are no options and alternatives, then hospital admission is likely to become the common way of managing acute mental health crises.

Phase 2: Planning

Through assessment and information gathering the team found the information (shown in Box 2) to assist in making a decision as to the future care of Ms G.

Box 2: Information to aid the planning of care for Ms G	
Historical information	**Network of care**
❖ Currently a student at a local university studying journalism. Immediately prior to her current symptoms, she had been on holiday with a number of friends to an outdoor music festival (two weeks before). While there she is reported to have smoked excessive amounts of cannabis, and claims to have taken LSD and Ecstasy. ❖ There is no record of any past psychiatric history. It has been stated that she regularly smokes cannabis. ❖ GP reports that there is a medical history of hyperthyroidism which has been controlled by medication. It is not clear whether she is currently taking medication.	❖ On assessment she is staying with a friend who, although supportive, is one of the people supplying her with cannabis and has continued to do so despite her recent behaviour and in fact felt that she was more relaxed when she smoked cannabis. ❖ Divorced from the father of her children four years ago. She has not seen him during this time. ❖ Her sister lives 50 miles away and works as a psychologist. Ms G has always kept in touch and seen her every two to three weeks. She has limited contact with her father (every two months or so) who lives locally. They have not got on for the last three years ❖ Current stressors include having difficulty looking after children, who have not been to school for three days. Her house is in a state of disrepair. She is having difficulty managing her finances and is in major debt. She is also having difficulty in completing her course work, and has had difficulty for the past six months.

Presenting the information in this way clarifies the current stressors for Ms G and her social system, which would direct the plan of care.

Who is involved in planning the care?

An initial plan was developed by the assessors with Ms G and her friend. They stated clearly what the team could offer, when they would next visit and how to contact the team at any time. The assessment and initial plan was then presented to the team at the daily handover meeting, to enable clarification for team members and a team plan of care to be developed.

The daily handover meeting needs to be prioritised by all team members. It is essential in the CRHT team approach that all team members are aware of each case and that the broader team is actively involved in developing plans.

Effective management of risk is an essential component of a CRHT team's work. Strategies need to be in place to ensure that decisions about individual cases are made by the team to avoid defensive practice and to encourage positive risk taking.

Adopting a 'named worker' approach for each case ensures consistency. This individual is responsible for making sure a plan is in place. Although they will not be the only person involved in face-to-face work with the service user, they are a point of contact for them and the rest of their social system. Where a care co-ordinator exists in the CMHT, the named worker will be responsible for making certain that they are involved in the planning process, either through attendance at CMHT meetings, by holding separate reviews or through joint visiting, or a combination of all of these. Developing joint working protocols between these teams can be helpful in ensuring good communication takes place.

In the case of Ms G, who was not already in touch with mental health services, a decision needed to be made at an early stage as to whether she would require ongoing support once the crisis was resolved. In view of the severity of the symptoms and the nature of her current stressors, it was felt that ongoing support in the medium term (approximately six months at least) would be required. Referral to the CMHT for allocation of a care co-ordinator was therefore requested. An agreement had been previously reached with the CMHT that priority would be given to those individuals referred from the acute inpatient unit and the CRHT team. This ensured the speedy allocation of cases.

Where do service users and carers fit into the planning process?

Because a CRHT team works predominately with people in the community, its relationship with service users is significantly different from that which exists in the inpatient unit. The team will attempt to involve all parties in the decision-making process but the main difference is in the need to negotiate a plan of action. Both service users and carers have commented on how much more involved they feel in the process and how their understanding of the crisis has been enhanced.

Phase 3: Intervention

These are some of the key interventions which led to the resolution of the crisis for Ms G.

❖ She was taken on by the crisis team and agreed to visits twice daily.

❖ Initially commenced on medication in an attempt to alleviate her symptoms and assist in establishing a regular sleep pattern.

❖ Contact was made with her sister, who met with the team and agreed to look after the children, initially for two days to give respite. This had been identified as necessary in the risk assessment.

❖ A general physical examination was carried out on initial assessment including blood tests to check thyroid function. This was found to be overactive and required immediate and ongoing treatment.

❖ An attempt was made to help Ms G to return to her own flat, as her friend also had children and the environment was not conducive to recovery. Ms G had lost the keys to her own flat, and the team contacted the housing department to arrange access to the flat and for various repairs to be completed.

❖ The team reviewed Ms G's finances and arranged an appointment with a debt counsellor.

❖ Symptoms reduced over a two- to three-week period and Ms G was again able to care for her children. She had difficulty getting the children to school, which is two miles away, so arrangements had to be made to ensure that this happened.

❖ Longer-term issues were identified. She wanted to move house as she was very isolated. This meant the children would need to change schools (the social worker in the CMHT agreed to assist with this). Discussion took place as to the effects of drug use on her mental health. The team carried out extensive liaison with family members, with the children's school and with the university regarding her course.

❖ As symptoms reduced the team was able to reduce its visits. Crisis team input lasted two months with follow-up from the CMHT care co-ordinator and a medical review at the outpatient clinic. The care co-ordinator was able to follow through issues regarding debt and housing, as well as monitoring continued improvement in Ms G's mental state.

There are a number of important issues about these interventions which it is hoped will give an insight into the nature of working in CRHT teams.

One issue which was important at an early stage was the need to get the children re-established at school. Social services teams, who might have been able to help, were not able to set anything up in the short term and the team considered how they might assist. They decided to drive Ms G and her children to and from the school for five days, while alternative services were engaged. There was significant disagreement within the team as to whether they should do this. The main concern was about the insurance, but the benefits were considerable:

❖ The children maintained their schooling.

❖ The fact that the children were at school each day changed the perception of the risk involved in working with the case. Initial concerns were raised about the risk to the children and indeed this was one of the major reasons for referral for hospital admission. The risks could be significantly reduced if the children were out of the house for eight hours a day.

❖ It enabled the team to spend periods of time on a one-to-one basis with Ms G without any distractions.

This demonstrates the flexible way in which CRHT teams work and highlights the impact of practical and social interventions on the mental health crisis.

Another important issue was the lack of clarity about what had caused this mental health crisis. Was it a consequence of substance use? Was it the stress of her course work? Was it because of her isolation in her home environment and her debts? Was it related to her physical health? Or was it a combination of some or all of these? This remained unknown throughout her time with the team and so the team had to work on all of these areas.

The involvement of drugs in a presentation has a tendency to lead staff to pre-judge the case with the suggestion that the individual must face the consequences of their own actions. It is important that teams keep an open mind and work with what is presented to them.

Phase 4: Resolution

The resolution stage is often neglected as once the level of the crisis is reduced teams often strive to pass people on to other services as quickly as possible. The consequence of doing this is often a fairly rapid return to a crisis situation. Time needs to be dedicated to working on the resolution phase and certain tasks should be completed prior to discharge or transfer to another team.

Ongoing evaluation of the interventions carried out is essential to monitor improvement and identify progress in managing the crisis. This can be done either in an informal manner by the named worker, or more formally through multidisciplinary clinical reviews or through handover meetings. Care needs to be taken to ensure handovers are a transfer of the important information and do not become in-depth discussion on every case, as time would not allow for this. Separate clinical reviews are suggested as the most appropriate forum for more in-depth discussion.

Maintaining the involvement of care co-ordinators throughout the team's intervention is essential in ensuring a smooth transfer of cases. It should not come as a shock to the care co-ordinator that their client is being transferred from the CRHT team if they have maintained input and had discussions with the team throughout the acute episode.

Visits and input from the team should be reduced prior to discharge or transfer from the team. Taking Ms G as an example, if the team had maintained two visits a day throughout its input and then sought to transfer to the care co-ordinator, the likelihood is that the care co-ordinator could see her only fortnightly. There is a major imbalance here which would very likely lead to a rapid relapse. A much better way of doing this is for the team to reduce its visits as the crisis begins to subside, and taper off visits prior to transfer. In Ms G's case, the team would have reduced their visits to once a week for the fortnight prior to discharge.

Emphasis needs to be placed on relapse prevention strategies and discussion about the early warning signs of a future mental health crisis. Information also needs to be given to both the service user and their carers about how to get help if there is a relapse to ensure that there is earlier intervention in the future.

The team should evaluate their intervention at the point of transfer and consider what worked well and what did not. This should be seen as a learning experience for the team as well as the service user and carers.

The GP should also be informed about the transfer and given relevant information about interventions and planned follow-up.

Whole system working

Much is said about the need for integrated services but one of the potential downsides of creating different teams for different functions is the risk of fragmentation. Why does this happen?

❖ Teams develop their own ethos and may have very different aims and objectives from one another, which may lead to conflict. The Mental Health Policy Implementation Guides (DH, 2001a, 2001b, 2001c) for the new CRHT, assertive outreach and early intervention teams do not help with this situation as often there is a lack of consistency. It appears that each guideline has been written in isolation.

❖ Teams may not understand their own role and purpose within the whole system and may be unclear about their target population.

❖ Teams may have unrealistic expectations about other teams' purposes and roles within the whole system, as well as their target populations. This leads to gaps in service provision or duplication, with different teams doing the same things.

❖ Rigid exclusion criteria and a general lack of flexibility causes conflict between teams and ultimately leaves service users in 'limbo' and confused as to how the system works.

We have found that there is a clear fragmentation in the way different teams work in many of the services we have visited. Each team is set up in isolation from the rest of the service, with no systematic way of communicating with other teams and insufficient understanding of how their objectives fit together with the rest of the system to meet the overall objectives of the service as a whole. As a consequence, conflict between teams is commonplace.

Where the interface between the teams is very clear, each team has specified aims and objectives which when put together meet the whole service's objectives. There is no duplication of roles and there is clarity as to how the teams communicate with one another. For this to exist the following need to be in place:

❖ Practitioners from all teams need not only to be aware of their own team's role, purpose and target population, but also to understand the same about the other teams in the system.

❖ Regular forums for face-to-face contact and case discussion between teams are essential both to gain a common understanding and to build effective working relationships.

❖ Clarity needs to be sought as to what each team expects of the others, with unrealistic expectations being challenged and a written agreement about how communication will take place.

❖ The written protocol should cover pathways for communication at each stage of the unique interface between teams. For a known case between the CRHT team and CMHT, for example, the interfaces lie at the point of referral from the CMHT to the CRHT team, in the ongoing input from the CRHT team and at the point of transfer back to the CMHT. At each stage of this process both teams should negotiate how communication should best take place.

By using the case study of Ms G we have attempted to demonstrate how CRHT teams can work through the crisis in a structured way, identifying some of the key activities in which teams engage. To conclude and summarise, we give our top tips for CRHT teams. These are in no particular order of importance.

Top tips for effective crisis resolution home treatment

❖ Target those who would otherwise be admitted to hospital.

❖ All team members should be involved in developing the referral form to be used by the team.

❖ Defining the crisis in a social systems context is essential as this will be the initial focus of the intervention.

❖ An early decision has to be made as to whether the referral represents a crisis that requires acute intervention.

❖ Where acute intervention is indicated, decisions as to where this takes place will depend on the resources available to the team.

❖ CRHT teams often rely on the support and co-operation of carers and at the assessment stage it is important to clarify their view of the crisis, the implications for them and how they might be involved in resolving it.

❖ The interventions a team will be able to provide will be contingent on the skills to deliver these being readily available to the team.

❖ A decision should be made regarding hospital admission after the assessing practitioners have weighed up the relative benefits of the range of options they have at their disposal in terms of the venue for treatment/intervention.

❖ Teams should attend each assessment with the expectation that the person will be treated at home, and only when it is clear that this is not a viable option should hospital admission be considered.

❖ The daily handover meeting needs to be prioritised by all team members. It is essential in the CRHT team approach that all team members are aware of each case and that the broader team is actively involved in developing plans.

❖ CRHT is part of a wider system of care delivery and as such is dependent on the wider system for its effectiveness.

❖ An agreement should be reached with the CMHT that priority will be given to individuals referred from the acute inpatient unit and CRHT team. This will ensure speedy allocation of cases.

❖ CRHT teams should be seen to be offering a bio-psycho-social approach to their interventions.

❖ Teams should ensure that time is dedicated to working on the resolution phase.

❖ Teams should secure the involvement of care co-ordinators from other teams such as the CMHT during the time that they are working with the service user.

❖ Visits and input from the team should be reduced prior to discharge/transfer from the team.

❖ Emphasis should be placed on relapse prevention strategies and there should be discussion about the early warning signs for a future mental health crisis to enhance the ability of the individual, their social system and services to manage a future relapse.

Conclusion

This manual has drawn on the broad experiences of those practising in and delivering training to CRHT teams nationally. It is based on our experiences so far. There are many challenges and opportunities ahead. Among other things a national survey to benchmark the functioning of CRHT teams is in the process of completion. This will give us a clear picture as to the characteristics of CRHT teams and identify areas for future development.

The belief that the hard work is done and that it is time to turn to other priorities is a threat which needs to be challenged at all levels. The energy and drive from practitioners working in CRHT teams, from managers and indeed from central government in ensuring that CRHT has remained high on the agenda has been crucial in its successful implementation. This must be built on, not lost, as we move to sustain and improve services in the coming years.

References

Atkinson, C. & Zwick, R. (1982) The Client Satisfaction Questionnaire: Psychometric properties and correlations with service utilization and psychotherapy outcome. *Evaluation & Programme Planning*, 5: 233-237.

Barton, R. (1976) *Institutional neurosis* (Third edition). Bristol: John Wright.

Birchwood, M. & Drury, V. (1995) Using the crisis. In: Phelan, M., Strathdee, G. & Thornicroft, G. (eds) *Emergency Mental Health Services in the Community*. Cambridge: Cambridge University Press, 116-148.

Bridgett, C. & Polak, P. (2003a) Social systems intervention and crisis resolution. Part 1: Assessment. *Advances in Psychiatric Treatment*, 9: 424-431.

Bridgett, C. & Polak, P. (2003b) Social systems intervention and crisis resolution. Part 2: Intervention. *Advances in Psychiatric Treatment*, 9: 432-438.

Bristol Mind (2004) *Crisis ... What crisis? The experience of being in a crisis in Bristol*. Bristol: Mind.

Caplan, G. (1964) *Principles of Preventative Psychiatry*. London: The Tavistock Institute.

Care Services Improvement Partnership (2006) *The 10 High Impact Changes for Mental Health Services*. London: CSIP.

Cohen, C.I. (2000) Overcoming Social Amnesia: The role for a Social Perspective in Psychiatric Research and Practice. *Psychiatric Services*, 51: 72-78.

Dean, C. & Gadd, E.M. (1990) Home Treatment for acute psychiatric illness. *British Medical Journal*, 301: 1021-1023.

Dean, C., Phillips, J., Gadd, E.M., Joseph, M., & England, S. (1993) Comparison of community based service with hospital based service for people with acute severe psychiatric illness. *British Medical Journal*, 307: 473-476.

Department of Health (1998) *Modernising Mental Health Services: Safe, Sound and Supportive*. London: DH.

Department of Health (1999) *The National Service Framework for Mental Health: Modern Standards and Service Models*. London: DH.

Department of Health (2000a) *The NHS Plan: A Plan for Investment, A Plan for Reform*. London: DH.

Department of Health (2000b) *Effective Care Co-ordination in Mental Health Services: Modernising the Care Programme Approach. A Policy Booklet*. London: DH.

Department of Health (2001a) *The Mental Health Policy Implementation Guide: Crisis Resolution/ Home Treatment Teams*. London: DH.

Department of Health (2001b) *The Mental Health Policy Implementation Guide: Assertive Outreach*. London: DH.

Department of Health (2001c) *The Mental Health Policy Implementation Guide: Early Intervention in Psychosis*. London: DH.

Department of Health (2001d) *Safety First: Five Year Report of the National Confidential Inquiry into Suicide and Homicide by People with Mental Illness*. London: DH.

Department of Health (2002a) *The Mental Health Policy Implementation Guide: Adult Acute Inpatient Care Provision*. London: DH.

Department of Health (2002b) *The Mental Health Policy Implementation Guide: Community Mental Health Teams*. London: DH.

Department of Health (2005) *New ways of working for psychiatrists: enhancing effective, person centred services through new ways of working in multi-disciplinary and multi-agency contexts*. London: DH.

Fenton, F.R., Tessier, L., Contandriopoulos, A.P., Nguyen, H. & Struening, E.L. (1982) A comparative trial of home and hospital psychiatric treatment: financial costs. *Canadian Journal of Psychiatry*, 27 (3): 177-187.

Fish, L. (1971) Using Social-Systems Techniques on a Crisis Unit. *Hospital and Community Psychiatry*, 22: 252-255.

Ford, R. & Kwakwa, J. (1996) Rapid reaction, speedy recovery. *Health Service Journal*, 18 April, 30-31.

Forrest, E. (2005) Stand by your beds. *Health Service Journal*, 15 September, 2-3.

Fraser, S.W. & Greenhalgh, T. (2001) Coping with complexity: educating for capability. *British Medical Journal*, 323: 799-803.

Fulford, K.W.M. (2004) Ten Principles of Values-Based Medicine. In: Radden, J. (ed) *The Philosophy of Psychiatry: A Companion*. New York: Oxford University Press.

Garcia, I., Kennett, C., Quraishi, M. & Durcan, G. (2005) *Acute Care 2004: A National Survey of Adult Psychiatric Wards in England*. London: The Sainsbury Centre for Mental Health.

Glover, G., Gerda, A. & Kannan, S.B. (2006, forthcoming) Crisis resolution/home treatment and psychiatric admission rates in England. *British Journal of Psychiatry*, 189. In Press.

Gray, P. & Baulcombe, S. (1996) Crisis de Coeur. *Health Service Journal*, 9 May, 24-25.

Hoult, J., Reynolds, I., Charbonneau-Powis, *et al.* (1983) Psychiatric hospital versus community treatment: the results of a randomized trial. *Australian and New Zealand Journal of Psychiatry*, 17: 160-167.

Hoult, J. (1986) Community care of the acutely mentally ill. *British Journal of Psychiatry*. 149: 137-144.

Johnson, S., Nolan, F., Pilling, S., Sandor, A., Hoult, J., McKenzie, N., White, I.R., Thompson, M. & Bebbington, P.M., (2005) Randomised controlled trial of acute mental health care by a crisis resolution team: The North Islington study. *British Medical Journal*, 331: 599-562.

Johnson, S., Nolan, F., Hoult, J., White, I.R., Bebbington, P., Sandor, A., McKenzie, N. & Patel, S.N. (2005) Outcomes of crises before and after the introduction of a crisis resolution team. *British Journal of Psychiatry*, 187: 68-75.

Jones, M. (1968) *Social Psychiatry in Practice*. Harmondsworth: Penguin Books.

Joy, C.B., Adams, C.E. & Rice, K. (2004) Crisis intervention for people with severe mental illnesses. *The Cochrane Database of Systematic Reviews 2004, Issue 4*. John Wiley & Sons Ltd.

Kennedy, H. (2001) Risk assessment is inseparable from risk management. *Psychiatric Bulletin*, 25: 208-211.

Mind (2004) *Ward Watch: Mind's campaign to improve hospital conditions for mental health patients*. London: Mind.

Minghella, E., Ford, R., Freeman, T., Hoult, J., McGlynn, P. & O'Halloran, P. (1998) *Open all Hours: 24 Hour response for people with mental health emergencies.* London: The Sainsbury Centre for Mental Health.

Ministry of Health for New Zealand (1998) *Guidelines for Clinical Risk Assessment and Management in Mental Health Service.* Ministry of Health for New Zealand

Morgan, S. (2000) *Clinical Risk Management: A Clinical Tool and Practitioner Manual.* London: The Sainsbury Centre for Mental Health.

Morgan, S. & Hemming, M. (1999) Risk Management and Community Treatment Orders. *Mental Health Care*, 31: 20.

Morrice, J.K.W. (1968) Emergency Psychiatry. *British Journal of Psychiatry*, 114: 485-491.

Muijen, M., Marks, I.M., Connolly, J. & Audini, B. (1992) Home-based care and standard hospital care for patients with severe mental illness: A randomised controlled trial. *British Medical Journal*, 304: 749-754.

Muir, H. & O'Hara, M. (2005) Risk Strategy. *The Guardian* (*Society* supplement), 9 March, 6-7.

National Institute for Clinical Excellence (2004) *Self-harm: The short-term physical and psychological management and secondary prevention of self-harm in primary and secondary care.* Clinical Guideline 16. London: National Institute for Clinical Excellence.

New, B. (1999) *A Good Enough Service: Values, Trade-offs and the NHS.* London: Institute for Public Policy Research.

National Institute for Mental Health in England (2004) *The Ten Essential Shared Capabilities: A framework for the whole of the mental health workforce.* Leeds: NIMHE.

Oxford University Press (2001) *Oxford Dictionary Thesaurus.* Oxford: Oxford University Press.

Pasamanick, B., Scarpitti, F.R. & Dintz, S. (1967) *Schizophrenics in the community: An experimental study in the prevention of hospitalization.* New York: Appleton-Century-Crofts.

Petch, E. (2001) Risk Management in UK Mental Health Services: An overvalued idea? *Psychiatric Bulletin*, 25: 203-205.

Polak, P.R. (1967) The Crisis of Admission. *Social Psychiatry*, 2 (4): 150-157.

Polak P. (1970) Patterns of Discord: Goals of Patients, Therapists, and Community Members. *Archives of General Psychiatry*, 23: 277-283.

Polak, P. (1972) Techniques of Social Systems Intervention. *Current Psychiatric Therapies*, 12: 185-193.

Polak, P. & Jones, M. (1973) The Psychiatric Non-hospital: A Model for Change. *Community Mental Health Journal,* 9 (2):123-132.

Protheroe, D. & Carroll, A. (2001) Twenty-four hour crisis assessment and treatment teams: too radical for the UK? *Psychiatric Bulletin*, 25: 416-417.

Rapp, C. (1998) *The Strengths Model: Case Management with people suffering from severe and persistent mental illness.* Oxford: Oxford University Press.

Reding, G.R. & Raphelson, M. (1995) Around the clock mobile psychiatric crisis intervention: Another effective alternative to psychiatric hospitalization. *Community Mental Health Journal*, 31: 179-190.

Rix, S. & Shepherd, G. (2003) Acute Wards: problems and solutions. *Psychiatric Bulletin*, 27: 108-111.

Rokeach, M. (1973) *The Nature of Human Values.* New York: The Free Press.

Rosen, A. (1997) Crisis management in the community. *Medical Journal of Australia*, 167: 633-638.

Ryan, T. (1998) Perceived risks associated with mental illness: beyond homicide and suicide. *Social Science and Medicine*, 46 (2): 287-297.

Sackett, D.L., Straus, S.E., Scott Richardson, W., Rosenberg, W. & Haynes, R.B. (2000) *Evidence-Based Medicine: How to Practice and Teach EBM* (2nd edition). Edinburgh and London: Churchill Livingstone.

SCMH (1998) *Acute Problems. A survey of the quality of care in acute psychiatric wards*. London: The Sainsbury Centre for Mental Health.

SCMH (2001) *Mental Health Topics: Crisis Resolution*. London: The Sainsbury Centre for Mental Health. (Web paper. Available from www.scmh.org.uk)

SCMH/MHAC (1997) *The National Visit: A one-day visit to 309 acute psychiatric wards by the Mental Health Act Commission in collaboration with the Sainsbury Centre for Mental Health*. London: The Sainsbury Centre for Mental Health.

Sharpe, C. (1997) *The origin and evolution of Human Values*. DP Press Ltd.

Smyth, M.G. (2003) Crisis resolution/home treatment and inpatient care. *Psychiatric Bulletin*, 27: 44-47.

Social Exclusion Unit (2004) *Mental Health and Social Exclusion*. London: ODPM.

Stein, L. I. & Test, M. A. (1980) Alternatives to mental hospital: A conceptual model, treatment program and clinical evaluation. *Archives of General Psychiatry*, 37: 392-397.

Sutherby, K. & Szmukler, G. (1995) Community Assessment of Crisis. In: Phelan, M., Strathdee, G. & Thornicroft, G. (eds) *Emergency Mental Health Services in the Community*. Cambridge: Cambridge University Press, 149-173.

Sutherby, K., Szmukler, G., Halpern, A., Alexander, M., Thornicroft, G., Johnson, C. *et al.* (1999) A study of "crisis cards" in a community psychiatric service. *Acta Psychiatrica Scandinavica*, 100: 56-61.

Szmukler, G. (2003) Risk Assessment: "numbers" and "values". *Psychiatric Bulletin*, 27: 205-207.

Tyrer, P., Morgan, J., van Horn, E., Jayakody, M., Evans, K., Brummell, R. *et al.* (1995) A randomised controlled study of close monitoring of vulnerable psychiatric patients. *Lancet*, 345: 756-759.

Tyrer, P., Sensky, T. & Mitchard, S. (2003) Principles of nidotherapy in the treatment of persistent mental and personality disorders. *Psychotherapy and psychosomatics*, 72 (6): 350-356.

von Bertalanffy, L. (1968) *General System Theory*. New York: George Braziller Inc.

Wing, J.K., Beevor, A.S, Curtis, R.H., Park, S.B., Hadden, S. & Burns, A. (1998) Health of The Nation Outcome Scales (HONOS). Research and Development. *British Journal of Psychiatry*, 172: 11-18.

Woodbridge, K. & Fulford, K.W.M. (2004) *Whose Values? A workbook for values-based practice in mental health care*. London: The Sainsbury Centre for Mental Health.

Young, L. & Reynolds, I. (1981) *Evaluation of Selected Psychiatric Admission Wards*. New South Wales: Division of Health Service Research, Health Commission of New South Wales.